STRUCTURES
for
ARCHITECTS

B. S. Benjamin

Associate Professor of Architecture and
Architectural Engineering
School of Architecture and Urban Design
The University of Kansas

Ashnorjen Bezaleel Publishing Company

The Home of Fine Publishing

U.S.A.

Published by
Ashnorjen Bezaleel Publishing Co.
2612 Stratford Road, Lawrence, Kansas 66044

PRINTED IN THE UNITED STATES OF AMERICA BY THE
UNIVERSITY OF KANSAS PRINTING SERVICE

Preface

This book is intended to serve as a good text for the sequence of courses in "structures" that architectural students are required to take in the course of their undergraduate architectural education. The Author's experience in teaching architectural students has shown that most of them approach the subject with some element of dislike and a little fear based on the irrational assumption that "structures" is not really related to the main courses in architectural design that form the core of their curriculum. Very often they are justified in both their dislike and their fears for when they do learn the subject they are introduced to courses from a strictly engineering point of view and which appear to be divorced from their architectural design sequence—not supportive to it.

This book attempts to overcome these handicaps by treating the subject as a supportive course and attempting to integrate it into the main architectural design courses. It does so by attempting to meet the following objectives:

1. It attempts to answer in the body of the book the structural questions that the student is likely to meet within his architectural designs. The student is encouraged, through 'Problems for Solution,' to apply his knowledge and to use structure as an element of design. In this aspect he can be assisted by his Architectural Instructors who could profitably set short, limited scope problems for this purpose.

2. It attempts to emphasise the structural behavior of the system as an essential requirement for its analysis and design. To do so it encourages the student to verbalise the behavior of his structural system. If he is successful in doing this, he has gone a long way towards understanding it.

3. There is an entire chapter that has been devoted to the use of Handbooks for the design of pre-engineered structural systems. It is hoped that this will legitimise this aspect of structural design as an important part of the architectural student's education. The chapter does not appear however,

until basic structural principles, materials and systems have been thoroughly studied.

4. The book is not overly mathematical. Instead a physical explanation of formulae has been given to enable the architectural student to understand the principles involved.

5. A special emphasis has been placed on relating the structural theory and design to specific materials such as steel, concrete or timber. The Codes have been referred to when necessary, but modifications and simplifications have been introduced. The architectural student needs to understand the requirements of the Codes, but himself requires only approximately correct answers. The Architect is not a Structural Engineer. This book attempts to make him into a good Architect—not convert him into a third-rate Structural Engineer! To attempt to do the latter only results in performing a disservice to both professions.

6. Finally the overall objective has been met, it is hoped, by a proper choice of material and by the manner and order in which specific topics have been treated to correlate the textbook with the teaching of the subject in the classroom.

Whilst the book has been written as a text, it is hoped that it will prove of value to the profession and will help practising Architects to clarify and reinforce structural principles, analysis and design. For structural design however, in the end, the final authorities are the Codes themselves and the Architect is encouraged to refer to them. The various Institutes such as the American Institute of Steel Construction, the American Concrete Institute and the American Institute of Timber Construction have all done an excellent job to rationalise design in their separate materials and without the research and design leadership provided by them, the state of the art would have lagged far behind the requirements of the Structural Engineer or Builder. The American Institute of Timber Construction in addition, makes special efforts to encourage the use of timber by Architects and Engineers. They have done so by distributing free literature and holding special seminars at Universities and the Author has helped to organise these at the University of Kansas. Timber as a structural material has its own potential for the Architect and has been rather neglected in past treatment of the subject.

In the writing of this book I have been helped by several individuals and I should like to express my gratitude to my wife for the typing of the manuscript and for part of the proof reading, to Dr. William "Max" Lucas, Jr., Associate Dean of the School of Architecture and Urban Design and of the Department of Architectural Engineering for his constant help and friendly encouragement, to Mr. William Smith and his staff at the K.U.

Printing Service who did an excellent and speedy job in the printing of the book and to Mike Elliott, one of my former students, who helped to draw about ten of the diagrams in the book.

In the several months that have been spent in the writing and the preparation of the manuscript, my wife Nora and my children Ashley and Jennifer have also helped me considerably, mainly by giving up with good cheer, their legitimate demands on my time. Their help is very warmly appreciated.

B. S. BENJAMIN

Ph.D.(Lond), M.Sc.(Lond), B.E., D.I.C.,
C.Eng., M.I.Struct.E., Member SPE

Lawrence, Kansas 66044
November 1974

Contents

Chapter 1

STRUCTURES IN ARCHITECTURE

1.1 Introduction

Architecture has many definitions. In one way it may be defined as an attempt by man to control his physical environment, whilst providing for his own needs. The practical expression of this attempt results in the Architect designing buildings of various types—houses, schools, hospitals, synagogues, churches, offices, shopping centers, theaters, factories, etc. These practical expressions of his architecture stand out as semi-permanent reminders of his success—or of his failure—as an Architect. The thought processes, the search for client needs, the logic employed, the complex interrelationships of spaces involved, the programming, the simulation and the evaluation of various designs, all these—so vitally important to the final design—may lie buried in the office of the Architect. What remains for all to see is a physical built up structure that is made of concrete or steel or timber, clad in brick or stone or glass, roofed with a roof of some sort, which withstands the natural elements of snow and wind and rain and provides an enclosed—or unenclosed—space for the client. The Architect with the help of the Structural Engineer and the Builder has converted his ideas of form and shape and space into a building. Whereas all his ideas are subtly expressed and half hidden, his structure and his materials of construction may be quite exposed and totally visible for all to see. His structure has become a vital—and perhaps the most exposed part—of his architecture. The interface between architecture and structure is a fascinating field and one that needs to be explored more deeply. Structure should influence architecture by making it more rational and efficient—but it should not dictate architecture. With certain structural systems however, such as a tension cable net, the structure so dominates the entire design that at least the visible expression of the architecture is basically all structure.

1.2 Importance of structures to the Architect

The importance of a knowledge of structures to the Architect now becomes quite clear. He needs this knowledge in order that the practical expression of his architecture is both rational and efficient. The structural system which enables his architecture to withstand the loads imposed on it and the materials of construction if properly chosen, all may help to further the expression of his ideas in a rational and economical manner. If improperly chosen, his structural system and materials of construction may work against him. He may for instance wish to create an impression of airiness in his architecture and finds instead that he has created an architecture that expresses monolithic massiveness. And all by an improper choice of structure or of materials.

There are some who will argue that since an Architect always works with a consulting Structural Engineer—and since it is the Engineer in the end who will make the final decisions on the structural system or the sizes to be used—a knowledge of structures is not really necessary to the Architect. There are two great objections to such an argument. Firstly if the Architect knows no structures, he hands over his beautiful piece of architecture possibly to an unthinking, unfeeling Engineer who then proceeds to insert into it a structural system. The decisions taken by the Engineer and motivated by his own philosophy and training—such as pure economics or ease of calculation or construction—may be quite different from the Architect's overall philosophy as expressed in his architecture. Since in the end, the structural system and materials of construction may largely dictate the appearance of the building, what the Architect has done is to permit the Engineer to "rape" his architecture. The second and greater objection to the argument that Architects do not need to know structures is that the Architect may in fact be proposing a piece of architecture that is really not capable of being built at the price that his client is prepared to pay. In other words, his architecture has been a "pipe dream" and an intellectual exercise outside the realms of practical reality.

The Architect on the other hand who has an adequate background in structures will have used his knowledge, perhaps even unconsciously, in the initial stages of his design thereby arriving at a feasible and practical design. Furthermore in his consultations with the Structural Engineer, he will be able to converse and discuss intelligently the objectives he was hoping to achieve and be able to appreciate—and if necessary even resist—changes being suggested because he is now operating from a position of knowledge and strength.

1.3 Structural systems and the architectural design

It now becomes clear that the architectural design needs a structural system or systems which the Architect can use to conveniently, safely and economically transform that design into a structure which resists the elements and encloses spaces according to his original ideas. It is the initial architectural design therefore that provides the Architect with the first data of information to enable him to make rational choices. What are the spans involved? What are the shapes and sizes of his spaces? Does he want clear unobstructed space or is he prepared to accept—or in fact positively desires— column supports which puncture his spaces at regular intervals? Structural systems suitable for spans of 30 ft may be quite unsuitable for spans of 100 ft and vice versa. It is important to realise that whilst the architectural design has spans (or spaces) of its own, it is the spans that the Architect imposes on the structural system which influence its choice.

Consider for instance a large concourse such as the lobby area of a high rise hotel building, shown in plan in Fig. 1a. The lobby area is 60 ft × 90 ft and the architectural design shows this to be so. If the Architect is not prepared to accept internal columns as in Fig. 1b, the shorter span for his struc-

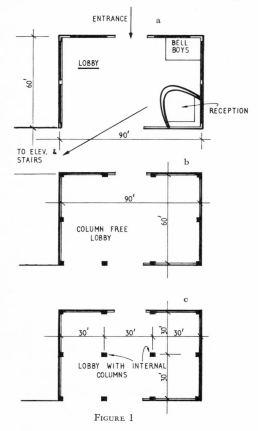

FIGURE 1

tural system is 60 ft. If however, he is prepared to accept internal columns in both directions at 30 ft centers, as in Fig. 1c, then the spans for his structural system are only 30 ft. He can have quite different structural arrangements for the two cases—even though his architectural design has remained unchanged. Spans are not the only data that can be gathered from the architectural design. Of equal importance is the realisation that the architectural design by its shape in plan and elevation, and by the objectives it hopes to achieve, can make positive input to suggesting entire structural systems as being more suited—or less suited—to the design itself. A tennis club facility with indoor courts, which requires that the headroom in the middle has to be considerably more than the headroom at the ends, may suggest that an arch structure or a pitched roof portal frame, as shown in Fig. 2, might be more suitable structural systems because they lend themselves more naturally to meeting headroom considerations. A cable structure, shown in Fig. 3, where the maximum sag occurs in the middle, may for the same reason be quite unsuitable.

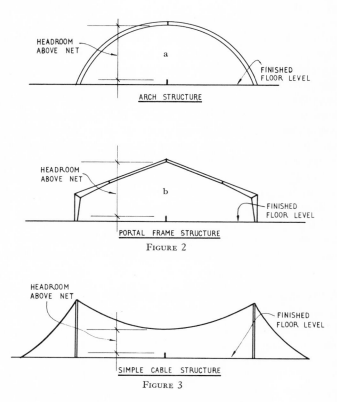

FIGURE 2

FIGURE 3

1.4 Structure and loads

The structural system, now an aesthetic part of the architectural design—and economically suitable for the spans involved—forms and supports enclosed spaces which are to meet the Architect's objectives and fulfill the needs of his client. The structure will be subjected to loads, both from inside and from outside the building. Loads from inside the building arise from the user and this may consist of **live loads** such as people, furniture, library bookstacks, automobiles, hospital beds, etc., or any combinations of these as appropriate. These loads arise from the use to which the space is to be put. Loads inside the building also arise from the **dead load** of the total construction itself. The structural system must be capable of taking its own load as also the loads imposed on it by flooring, permanent internal partitions, external cladding walls, ceilings, roofing, mechanical systems such as ducts, etc.

Loads from outside the building arise from the effects of the natural environment on the building. These may consist of **snow load** on the roof, **wind load** on the roof and sides and perhaps **earthquake loads.** It may be realised that these loads depend very largely on the location of the building. The snow load for which the building has to be designed in Arizona is vastly different from the snow load in North Dakota. The wind load in Florida is considerably more than the wind load in Kansas. If the building is not in an earthquake zone, these loads need not be considered at all.

All these loads, whether from inside or outside the building, whether arising from the building itself, the user or the natural elements, all have to be taken by the structural system from all points of application and in any manner in which they may be applied and transferred safely and economically to the foundations where they are then dissipated into the soil on which the building rests. This is the function of structure in architecture and its importance can hardly be underestimated. A badly designed structural system may not perform its function safely and collapse with catastrophic and disastrous consequences under normal overload conditions. Even if such an extreme situation does not result, a badly designed structural system may prove to be much more expensive than a comparatively efficient one.

1.5 Structure and materials of construction

It is now required to choose the materials of construction. Sometimes the choice is largely dictated by the fact that proven experience suggests that certain structural systems are compatible only with certain materials of construction. For instance, timber is totally unsuitable and incompatible as the main structural material in a high rise building. Such a building would require a structural system in steel or concrete. The incompatibility of the material of construction with the structural system chosen may be governed in some cases by the consideration that final sizes would be either too large or too small to warrant an economical structure. Incompatibility can be basically dictated by the nature of the construction material itself. All materials have certain characteristics in response to load which make them unique and the good Architect needs to exploit the strong characteristics of his building materials for proper design. For instance, steel is extremely strong in tension whereas concrete is not. Steel is also, for the strength it affords, a comparatively light structural material whereas concrete is heavy. The dead load of a steel structure is therefore quite small whereas the dead load of a concrete structure is quite large. A light, large span, cable net roof structure, which uses tension as the primary means of load propagation to transfer the loads from the roof towards the supports, is therefore very suitable in steel—but unsuitable in concrete.

The nature of the material is yet again, not the only reason for incompatibility between the structural system and the material of its construction. Varying degrees of incompatibility can arise from a number of reasons such as aesthetic requirements of the Architect, building code requirements (particularly the fire codes), easy availability or otherwise of materials, local methods and practices and finally economics.

1.6 Design of the structure

The Architect is now in a position to design his structure. He has a structural system he wishes to use, has estimated the loads that will be imposed on it and has chosen his material of construction. He cannot be fully sure however, whether his choices have been rational unless he is able to approximately size the members of his structural system to determine whether or not his structural system is going to be a feasible and economical one. Consider for instance the floors of a 30 storey high rise building. On designing his floors he finds that the structural depth of the floor, for the spans he is considering and for the reinforced concrete material he had in mind, is say 3 ft. Even a saving of 6 in. in the structural depth would reduce his building height by 15 ft! Should he try another structural material such as steel? Should he try perhaps another structural arrangement in the same type of structural system to reduce his structural depth? Should he go to an entirely different structural system altogether? Or should he alter his spans and perhaps compromise his architectural design? These are questions that the Architect cannot conceivably even begin to answer unless he is able to approximately design his structural system. The emphasis here is on the word **approximate.** A Structural Engineer will come along at a later date and accurately size his members for construction purposes, perhaps using more sophisticated methods of analysis. The Architect however needs an approximate size, not to be a structural engineer, but to better appreciate his structural system—thereby enabling him to improve his architectural design.

To design the structure, the Architect needs to fully appreciate two separate stages of design:

1. He needs to know how load propagates or flows through the various elements of his structure. This is **analysis.**

2. He needs to know how this propagation or flow of load affects the material of his structural element so that he can provide an adequate amount of material for the structural element to be safe. This is **sizing** and more properly **design.**

Let us consider each of these stages in greater detail.

1.6.1 Load propagation through the structural system

It has been seen that the structural system collects the loads from the points of application (snow load on the roof, wind load on the roof and sides, live or user loads on the floors, dead load everywhere, etc) and transmits them to the foundations. The load in fact propagates or flows from the point of application, with the help of structural mechanisms of load transfer, along and through the structural system to the foundations. The particular mechanism, or combination of mechanisms, that are used are of vital importance to a proper understanding of the behavior of the structural system and hence to a proper design of the structure.

As an example, consider a chandelier hanging by a chain or cable from a roof beam which rests on columns as shown in Fig. 4. The load of the

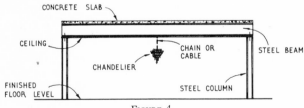

FIGURE 4

chandelier travels upwards through the mechanism of **tension** in the chain or cable to the underside of the beam. It then flows sideways (together with the dead load of the beam itself and the load from the slab) through the mechanisms of **bending moment** and **shear force** (the bending of the beam) to the columns where it is converted into end reactions or compressive forces which the beam imposes on the columns. Each column then, through the mechanism of **compression** transfers its share of the load (together with the dead load of the column itself) to the foundation as a compressive force on the soil where (together with the dead weight of the foundation itself) it is dissipated into the earth. The chain or cable which supports the chandelier is in **tension,** the beam is in **bending** and **shear** and the columns are in

compression. These mechanisms of load transfer will be considered in greater detail in Chapter 3.

A correct appreciation of load propagation, that is the determination of the correct path and manner in which the transfer and flow of load occurs, is of the utmost importance to an appreciation of the behavior of the structural system and hence to its analysis and design.

1.6.2 Effect of load propagation on the material

The load in its path through the structural system stresses and strains the material in various ways. An understanding of the manner in which this occurs is equally essential to the proper understanding of the structure. The material of the cable in Fig. 4 is under a **tensile stress** due to the tension in the cable. It therefore needs to have a sufficiently large area of cross section so that it does not snap. In fact what is being said is that the tensile stress in the material of the cable must be below the **ultimate tensile strength** of the material of the cable—with a certain **factor of safety.** The load of the chandelier can never increase and can be estimated with a fair degree of accuracy. Nevertheless a factor of safety of 1.4 or 1.5 must be applied to ensure that the cable is perfectly safe against defects in the material of the cable, defects in the workmanship, our ignorance of any extra loading that may be applied during the erection of the chandelier, our ignorance of the exact connections that will be used which could lead to overstressing, etc. The factor of safety is really our **factor of ignorance** which is applied to ensure that the structure is safe at all times and under all conditions.

There are two alternative ways of applying the factor of safety in structural design. In **working stress** design, this factor of safety is applied to the ultimate strength of the material to yield a **permissible stress** up to which the material can **safely** be stressed.

$$\text{Permissible stress} = \frac{\text{Ultimate strength}}{\text{Factor of safety}}$$

The load on the structure is then the **working load** or the load which the structure normally takes under all conditions of operation.

In **ultimate load** design however, the factor of safety is applied to the working load to yield a much larger load for purposes of design called the ultimate load.

$$\text{Ultimate load} = \text{Working load} \times \text{Factor of safety}$$

This ultimate load is a fictitious value, since it is **never** ever expected to be reached. The structure is then designed in such a way that the ultimate strength of the material would in fact be reached under this ultimate load—and collapse would occur.

Strength is not the only criterion of design. Deflections are equally important. The cable under the weight of the chandelier will be strained and will hence stretch by a small amount. The beam under its loading will bend or flex and hence deflect downwards. This deflection is transmitted back to the chandelier. The columns under their loading will compress by a small amount as well and this is transmitted back to the beam and the chandelier. The Architect has then to ensure that the total deflection of the chandelier is within permissible limits. Experience will show that the actual extension of the cable or the compression of the columns is very small and can be neglected, thereby leaving the deflection of the beam to conform to limits or regulations as laid down by the Building Codes.

1.7 Conclusion

The Architect has chosen his structural system and his materials of construction. He has now appreciated load propagation through his structural system and the effects of such load propagation on the material. He can then provide enough material (or in other words, a proper size of member) for all elements of his structure to ensure that the internal stresses developed are less than those permissible for the material in question. He can also ensure that the deflections that his structural members are going to have (as a result of strain) are again less than those permissible for the member. He has in fact sized his members safely and economically and in so doing has designed his structure.

The merits and demerits of his architectural design and the true cost of his piece of architecture to his client may also have become more apparent.

Chapter 2

STRUCTURE AND LOADS

2.1 The loading on a structure

It has been seen in 1.4 that a correct estimation of the loads acting on the structure are essential to the proper choice and design of the structural system. The various types of loadings that can act on a structure are as follows:

1. Dead load
2. Live load
3. Snow load
4. Wind load
5. Earthquake load
6. Water and earth loads

Each of these loads and the manner in which they act on the structure will now be briefly discussed.

2.2 Dead loads

The dead loads which act on the structure arise from the weight of the structure itself and from the weight of all the non-structural materials attached to it and which form the building. These non-structural items include the weights of roofing, waterproofing, ceilings, flooring, permanent internal partitions and cladding walls, finishings, etc. These non-structural loads can be estimated with a fair degree of accuracy since they involve mainly material weights and thicknesses. In this estimation the Architect is in an even better position than the Engineer, because the Engineer has to guess what the Architect will provide in the form of flooring, ceiling, etc, whereas the Architect knows precisely what flooring or ceiling material he is going to use.

The dead load that arises from the weight of the structure itself however, is considerably more difficult to estimate since the sizes of the structural members can only be accurately known **after** the design has been carried out. Both Architect and Engineer have therefore to make an intuitive guess as to the sizes of the members and after the design has been completed make a quick check to verify that the guess was a reasonable one. If it was, the design stands. If it was not, the dead load of the structural element or member is re-estimated more accurately and the design carried out all over again. With a little bit of experience, this recalculation is seldom necessary.

It can also be seen that in order to estimate the dead loads, whether they arise from the structural or non-structural components of the building, it is necessary to know material unit weights. For some common building materials, these are shown in Table 2.2.1. The conversion from unit material weights to actual loads on the structural member for purposes of design will be considered in greater detail in 2.9.

Table 2.2.1
MATERIAL WEIGHTS FOR SOME COMMON BUILDING MATERIALS

Material	Weight lbs/sq ft	Material	Weight lbs/sq ft
Roofs		**Floors**	
3 ply felt and gravel	5.5	Hardwood 1 in. nominal	4.0
5 ply felt and gravel	6.5	Plywood 1 in.	3.0
Corrugated steel	1-5	Ceramic tile	10.0
Corrugated aluminum	1.0	Linoleum	1.0
Corrugated asbestos	3.0	Vinyl tile	1.0
Plastics (FRP) sheet	0.5	Lightweight concrete 1 in.	5.0
Plywood sheathing 1 in.	3.0	Reinforced concrete 1 in.	12.0
Timber decking 2 in.	5.0	Metal deck	10.0
Timber decking 3 in.	8.0		
Timber decking 4 in.	10.0	**Walls and partitions**	
Asphalt shingles	2.0	Wood panelling 1 in.	2.5
Wood shingles	3.0	Plaster 1 in. on lath	10.0
Fiberglas rigid insulation	1.5	Wood studs 2 x 4, 12 in.—	
Expanded glass insulation	0.8	16 in. o.c.	2.0
Expanded polystyrene insulation	0.2	Brick masonry per 4 in.	40.0
Metal deck	2.0	Stone masonry per 4 in.	55.0
		Hollow concrete block	30.0
Ceilings		Steel partitions	4.0
Acoustical fiber tile	1.0	Windows complete	8.0
Suspended channel system	1.0		

2.3 Live loads

Live loads are the superimposed user or occupancy loads that the structure must carry in order to perform its function satisfactorily—and for which it was built in the first place. This can include the weight of people and furniture in a house, people and theater seats in a theater, people and library stacks in a library, people and hospital beds in a hospital, people and automobiles in a multi-storey car park, etc. This also includes the weight of all movable internal partitions, movable mechanical equipment, etc. The list is endless. In some cases the load may not be vertical but may be horizontal, as for instance in the design of a hand rail or the railing on a balcony.

The estimation of the live load can never be either fully accurate or fully complete since even the user can change with time, thereby altering the user or occupancy load during the life of the building.

Table 2.3.1

LIVE USER OR OCCUPANCY LOADS

User or type of occupancy	Uniform load lbs/sq ft
Assembly areas such as dance halls, gymnasiums, plazas, etc.	
Fixed seating	50
Moveable seating	100
Stage areas	125
Public exit facilities such as corridors, exit balconies, stairways, etc.	100
Hospitals	40–60
Libraries	
Reading rooms	60
Stack areas	125–150
Offices	50–80
Residential, including private houses, apartments and hotel guest rooms	40
School classrooms	40
Stores	
Retail stores	75–100
Wholesale stores	100–125

The problem of the estimation of the live, user or occupancy load is however really not all that complex. The Uniform Building Code provides a value of the load that should be used in different locations. For instance, in a residential high rise apartment building the U.B.C. suggests a value of 40 lbs/sq ft (of plan area) in the living areas, but a value of 100 lbs/sq ft in the corridors (which are busier areas where more people may be expected to congregate). As another example, the load suggested by the U.B.C. for libraries is 60 lbs/sq ft in the reading rooms, but 125 lbs/sq ft in the stack areas. The complete user or occupancy loads that must be used in design are given by the Uniform Building Code and this should always be referred to before commencing the design. A few simple values from the codes are given in Table 2.3.1.

2.4 Snow loads

The snow load is also a form of live load, but one that acts only on the roof of the structure. Since, as we have seen, the load travels towards the foundations, snow load in fact contributes loading on many structural elements below the roof as well.

The snow load on the structure depends on the location of the building. A structure in Northern Canada has to carry far heavier snow load than in Oklahoma or Texas. A structure in Southern California may not be required to carry any snow load at all.

The snow load for various regions of the United States is shown in the map in Fig. 5. These are the minimum basic snow loads and in some cases may have to be appropriately increased depending on actual elevation. The snow load in the mountains is higher than in the plains. Further snow retention with odd shaped roofs may well dictate the need for higher values. A sharply sloped roof on the other hand permits the use of lower values than given in Fig. 5.

The snow load acts vertically and only on the plan area of the roof.

2.5 Wind loads

The actual manner in which the wind load affects the structure is very complex since, among other factors, it depends on the shape of the building, surface quality, its elevation above ground, the amount of shelter afforded by surrounding buildings, etc. The basic wind pressure on a vertical surface once again depends on the location of the building. The wind load in Florida is far higher than the wind load in Kansas. This value of the wind pressure can be got from the Uniform Building Code or from other Handbooks on design such as the Manual of the American Institute of Timber Construction (AITC). This value may include a shape coefficient factor $C_D = 1.3$. The shape coefficient factor is a measure of the way in which wind acts on that particular shape of the building. Consider for instance a rectangular building as shown in Fig. 6a in plan. The pressure on the windward side is 0.9 and the suction on the leeward side is 0.4-0.5 giving a total shape coefficient C_D of 1.3-1.4. For a hexagonal building, shown in plan in Fig. 6b, the shape coefficient C_D is only 1.04 because as may be appreciated, the wind flows more easily past the building. The shape coefficient also applies to roofs in elevation. Consider the pitched roof shown in Fig. 7a. The wind exerts a pressure on the windward side of the roof but creates a suction (or uplift) on the leeward side. The value of C_D de-

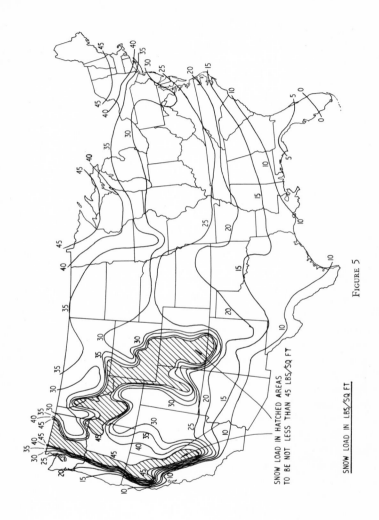

SNOW LOAD IN HATCHED AREAS
TO BE NOT LESS THAN 45 LBS/SQ FT

SNOW LOAD IN LBS/SQ FT

FIGURE 5

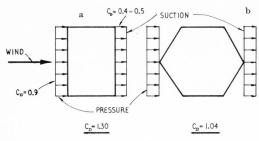

FIGURE 6

pends on the angle of pitch. When the roof is flat, as shown in Fig. 7b, the entire roof is in suction. This shows that in many cases the wind has a tendency to lift the roof off and the roof has therefore to be adequately anchored down against uplift. The shapes discussed are fairly simple shapes.

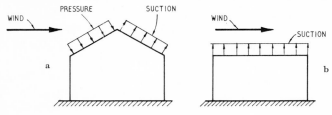

FIGURE 7

For very complex shapes, the wind pressure distribution on the building may have to be determined by wind tunnel tests on small models. A very complex tension roof structure is shown in Fig. 191 in Chapter 13. The contour lines of the shape coefficient factor C_D are shown on the plan of the roof in Fig. 8. The positive sign indicates pressure and the negative

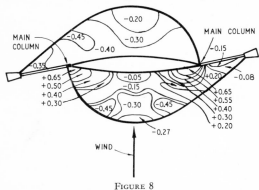

FIGURE 8

sign indicates suction. It can be seen that pressures are developed round the main columns but the rest of the roof is in suction. The tension structure itself will be discussed in greater detail in Chapter 13.

The basic wind pressures as obtained from the Uniform Building Code or from Design Handbooks is at a height of 30 ft above ground level. For high rise buildings or tall structures the design wind load has to be increased. This increase in the wind load with the height of the building is also given in the Uniform Building Code. A wind load of 30 lbs/sq ft at 30 ft above ground level has to be increased to 45 lbs/sq ft at 400 ft above ground level.

Very tall structures such as towers or chimney stacks, as also aerodynamically light structures such as cable tension nets, are further subjected to flutter or oscillation under gusting winds. This is a very complex problem in aerodynamics and the Engineer (not the Architect) in his final design of the structure will be required to have examined the problem very carefully.

2.6 Earthquake loads

Earthquake loads need only be taken into account in those areas or zones that are subject to severe earthquakes. For the United States, the zones from 1 to 3 are given in the map shown in Fig. 9. The different Codes differ slightly in their zoning and the Uniform Building Code shows a zone 0 as well. Nevertheless what the Codes do is to identify areas of the country where severe earthquakes may possibly occur. Texas is relatively free from earthquakes whereas California has a very real problem. The design of structures for earthquakes is a very complex dynamic problem and will once again be considered by the Engineer in his final analysis. Basically however, an earthquake results in an horizontal shake of the ground or foundation. The earth moves horizontally but the building or structure because of its weight or inertia resists such movement. This results in a horizontal force at every storey level of the building, the value of which dpends, amongst other things, on the weight of the building above it. The horizontal or shear forces increase towards the ground level where they are a maximum. The horizontal force at any storey level $\mathbf{V}$ can be given by the very approximate equation:

$$\mathbf{V} = \mathbf{Z}\,\mathbf{C_T}\,\mathbf{W} \quad\text{...}\quad 1$$

where,

$\mathbf{Z}$ = Zone coefficient for the different zones as given in Table 2.6.1

$\mathbf{C_T}$ = Coefficient that depends on the structural system used to absorb these horizontal forces

$\mathbf{W}$ = Weight of the building above that storey level.

It can be seen that the value of these horizontal forces depends on the type of structural system used to absorb these forces. Two such systems that may be used are shown in Fig. 10. A rigid frame structure is shown in Fig. 10a. The construction, which can be in steel or concrete, has rigid

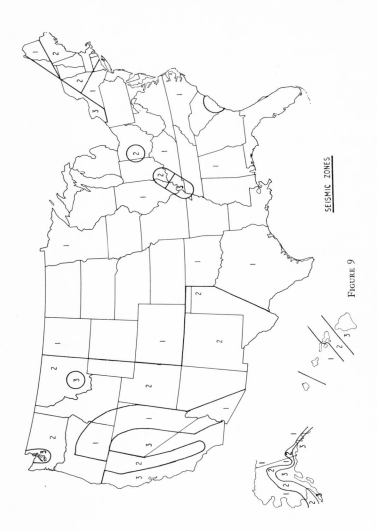

SEISMIC ZONES

FIGURE 9

Table 2.6.1
ZONE COEFFICIENTS

Coefficient Z	Zone 1	Zone 2	Zone 3
Z	0.25	0.50	1.00

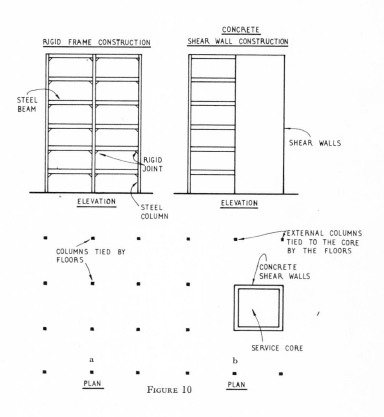

FIGURE 10

Table 2.6.2
VALUES OF COEFFICIENT C_T FOR SEISMIC DESIGN

Type of structure	No. of storeys				
	1	2	5	10	25
Shear walls	0.13	0.13	0.11	0.090	0.055
Rigid frame	0.07	0.07	0.05	0.035	0.025
Beam and column type systems with bracing and other building framing systems	0.10	0.10	0.08	0.060	0.040

joints between beam and column members. Fig. 10b shows shear wall construction with a concrete shear wall which extends the height of the building.
The Uniform Building Code specifies the value of the coefficients to be used
in Equation 1 and some modified typical approximate values are given in
Table 2.6.2. These structural systems and others for high rise buildings will
be discussed in greater detail in Chapter 8.

2.7 Water and earth loads

Water and earth loads have to be taken into account in the design of
those structures which are below ground such as retaining walls, basement
walls and floor slabs, some foundations, etc. They are really a form of live
load for such structures.

If the structure is entirely below water, the hydrostatic pressure is 62.4
lbs/sq ft, per foot of depth. The pressure distribution is linear and is shown
in Fig. 11a. If the load arises due to earth pressure, it is not as severe as
due to water since soil is generally capable of maintaining itself unaided
on a small slope, which is the angle of repose. This naturally depends on the
type of soil. Sand for instance, has a lower angle of repose than stiff clay.

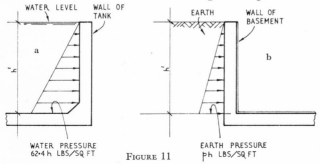

FIGURE 11

If however water enters into the clay, the picture changes considerably, since
the material now has a greater tendency to flow and hence exerts greater
earth pressure. In the absence of water, the soil pressure may be assumed as
25-35 lbs/sq ft per foot of depth. This is shown in Fig. 11b.

2.8 Combinations of load systems

The various loads that can individually act on the building have now
been analysed. It would be quite unrealistic however, to sum up all the
individual loads due to dead and live and snow and wind and earthquake
and then design the structure for the total. This would lead to a monstrously
large and over designed structure.

Consider a tall high rise building of say 20 stories. The dead load of
the building, structural and non-structural will always exist. It is now
conceivable that on some particular day, the entire building is full with its

intended user load, in every single room on all 20 storeys. Perhaps a convention has descended on the building and all the rooms are solidly booked up. (Most Building Codes allow for a reduction in floor loading when all storeys are being assumed to be fully loaded.) It is now not really conceivable that the full design load due to snow will fall on the roof at that time. It is even more impossible to suggest that a storm then develops with the full wind pressure acting on the sides and roof of the building at that time and it is totally absurd to then assume that an earthquake strikes the building!

For a rational design therefore, it is very essential to take realistic combinations of loadings that can occur together and the structural element be then designed for the worst case of these realistic combinations. When the action of the wind is being considered, most Building Codes permit, in Working Stress design, a 33% overstress or increase in the permissible stress that the material can take. In Ultimate Load design in concrete, the Ultimate load **U** for which the structural element has to be designed is given by,

$$\mathbf{U} = 0.75(1.4\ \mathbf{DL} + 1.7\ \mathbf{LL} + 1.7\ \mathbf{WL}) \ \text{..} \ 2$$

The factor of 1.4 is a factor of safety to the dead load and the factors of 1.7 are factors of safety for the live load and the wind load. The factor of 0.75 is in fact a method of **reducing** the total ultimate load for which the design is being carried out.

Earthquake loads (unless in zone 3) are generally not important and can be neglected by the Architect.

2.9 Conversion of unit loads into loads on the structure

The unit loads in lbs/sq ft of surface area or plan area for the various loadings such as dead, live, snow, wind, etc, can now be determined. Such unit loads however are of little use unless the Architect is able to convert them into actual loads on his structure or structural element. This is an easy process and a few examples are taken here to demonstrate the ease with which this conversion can be carried out.

Example 2.9.1

The floor of a corridor in an office building is shown in Fig. 12. The corridor is 8 ft wide, center to center of the steel beams. The beams carry a one-way reinforced concrete slab, assumed 5 in. thick. The floor has a light suspended accoustical tile ceiling and a vinyl tile finish on a 2 in. lightweight concrete topping. Determine,

    a. The total load on a 1 ft wide strip of slab,
    b. The total load on each of the supporting beams **AB.**

The loads on the floor per sq ft of plan area are first determined as follows:

Dead load

5 in. concrete slab (12 lbs/sq ft per 1 in. thickness) .... $= 60$ lbs/sq ft
2 in. lightweight concrete topping .... $= 16$ lbs/sq ft
Vinyl tile finish .... $= \ 1$ lbs/sq ft
Suspended tile ceiling .... $= \ 3$ lbs/sq ft

$$\text{Dead load Total} = \overline{80 \text{ lbs/sq ft}}$$

Live load

Corridor in an office building .... $= 100$ lbs/sq ft
No internal partitions

Total dead $+$ live load $= 80$ lbs/sq ft $+ 100$ lbs/sq ft $= 180$ lbs/sq ft.

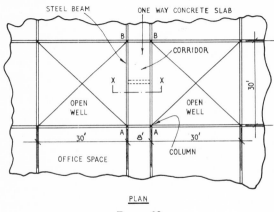

PLAN

FIGURE 12

a. Consider a strip of slab 1 ft wide shown dotted in Fig. 12. The load on every 1 ft of its length is therefore 180 lbs.

This can be written as 180 lbs/ft run (of the slab) as shown in the section in Fig. 13. This value can be used in design. Alternatively the total load on the entire 1 ft wide strip of slab can be obtained as,

$$\mathbf{W} = 180 \times 8 = 1440 \text{ lbs.}$$

b. The slab imposes a load on the beams **AB** that support it on each side and it is required to determine the total load on each of these beams. Since each of the beams has an open well on the other side, it follows that the only load on the beams is from the corridor. In the center section of the slab, over most of its length, the load is shared equally between the beams **AB**. Towards the ends however, the cross beams **AA** and **BB** take some of the load from the slab. This actual area which contributes load to the

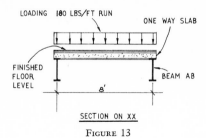

SECTION ON XX

FIGURE 13

beam **AB** is shown in Fig. 14. The load taken by the cross beams **AA** and **BB** can however be neglected in the design of beams **AB** and it can be assumed that the beams **AB** take **all** of the load from the slab.

The load on each beam is therefore,

$$\mathbf{W} = 180 \times \tfrac{1}{2} \text{ area of the slab}$$
$$= 180 \times 30 \times 4 = 21600 \text{ lbs.}$$

This total load can be converted to,

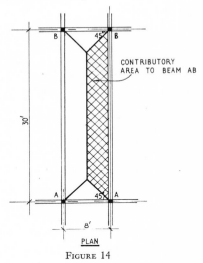

PLAN

FIGURE 14

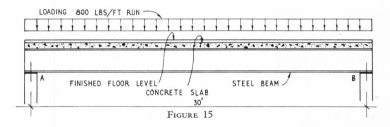

FIGURE 15

$$w \text{ lbs/ft} = \frac{21600}{30} = 720 \text{ lbs/ft}$$

If the dead load of the beam itself (together with any fireproofing) were assumed as 80 lbs/ft, the total design load on the main beam **AB** is 800 lbs/ft as shown in Fig. 15.

Example 2.9.2

A carport for an apartment complex in Southeast Kansas is required to roof three car spaces as shown in Fig. 16. It consists of light plastics roof sheeting (weight 1 lb/sq ft) supported on timber purlins 2 in. × 10 in. spaced 2 ft 9 in. on centers. The purlins span 16 ft and rest on two main timber glued laminated beams which span 27 ft 6 in. between timber posts 6 in. square and 10 ft high. The concrete foundation block for each post is 2 ft × 2 ft × 8 in. deep. If the timber weighs 36 lbs/cu ft, concrete weighs 144 lbs/cu ft and each main glued laminated beam weighs 30 lbs/ft determine,

   a. The total design load on any internal purlin in lbs,
   b. The total design load on one main beam in lbs,

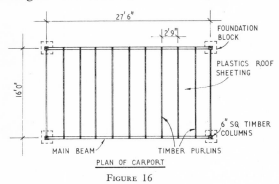

PLAN OF CARPORT

FIGURE 16

   c. The total design load on each timber post in lbs,
   d. The soil pressure beneath each foundation block in lbs/sq ft.

Referring to the map for snow load shown in Fig. 5, the snow load for the area in the problem may be assumed to be 20 lbs/sq ft. Since the roof is flat, the wind puts the roof in suction against its own dead load and may therefore be neglected.

$$
\begin{aligned}
\text{Snow load} &= 20 \text{ lbs/sq ft} \\
\text{Sheeting load} &= \underline{1 \text{ lbs/sq ft}} \\
\text{Total} &= 21 \text{ lbs/sq ft}
\end{aligned}
$$

   a. Superimposed load on one internal purlin is the total load on the contributory area to one purlin.

$$\mathbf{W} = 21 \times 16 \times 2.75 = 924 \text{ lbs}$$

Dead load of the purlin itself $= \dfrac{2}{12} \times \dfrac{10}{12} \times 16 \times 36 = 80 \text{ lbs}$

Total design load on one internal purlin $= 924 + 80 = 1004$ lbs.

b. In order to determine the load on each main beam, we determine the load that each purlin has imposed on the main beam as follows:

Load from an internal purlin on each main beam $= \dfrac{1004}{2} = 502$ lbs

The external purlins load directly on to the columns.

The total superimposed load on each main beam is the load imposed by 9 purlins.

$$\mathbf{W} = 502 \times 9 = 4518 \text{ lbs}$$

Dead load of each main beam $= 30$ lbs/linear ft $\times 27.5$ ft $= 825$ lbs

Total design load on each main beam $= 4518 + 825 = 5343$ lbs.

c. In order to determine the load on each timber post, we determine the load imposed by each main beam on the post and add the load from each external purlin as follows:

Load from each main beam on the post $= \dfrac{5343}{2} = 2672$ lbs

Load from external purlin $= \left(\dfrac{924}{2} + 80 \right) \times \dfrac{1}{2} = 271$ lbs

Total superimposed load on each post $= 2672 + 271 = 2943$ lbs

Dead load of the post itself $= \dfrac{6}{12} \times \dfrac{6}{12} \times 10 \cdot \times 36 = 90 \text{ lbs}$

Total design load on each timber post $= 2943 + 90 = 3033$ lbs.

d. In order to determine the soil pressure, it is necessary to determine the total load on the soil as follows:

Load from each post $= 3033$ lbs

Dead load of the concrete foundation block $= 2 \times 2 \times \dfrac{8}{12} \times 144 = 384$ lbs

Total load on the soil $= 3033 + 384 = 3417$ lbs

The soil pressure beneath each foundation block in lbs/sq ft is the load on the soil divided by the area over which the load is being dissipated which is $2 \times 2 = 4$ sq ft.

The soil pressure beneath each foundation block $= \dfrac{3417}{4} = 854$ lbs/sq ft.

If the soil is capable of taking this pressure without any settlement then the structure is safe.

As may be readily seen, the solutions of all problems of this nature are based on an estimation of the loads, the areas over which they act and an understanding of the manner in which load flows through the structural system in order to reach the foundations and be dissipated into the earth.

Problems for solution

Example 1: A two storey rectangular portal frame building in a town on the borders of North and South Dakota is shown in Fig. 17. It is acted upon by the wind. The portals are spaced at 20 ft centers. The cladding panels transfer the wind load to horizontal cladding rails which then load

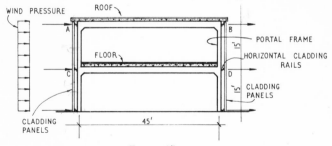

FIGURE 17

each portal at points **A, B, C** and **D**. For an internal portal, determine the load at each of these points.

Ans: Wind pressure 19.2 lbs/sq ft. C_D windward $= 0.9$, C_D leeward $= 0.4$. Load at **A** $= 2592$ lbs, load at **B** $= 1152$ lbs, load at **C** $= 5184$ lbs, load at **D** $= 2304$ lbs.

Example 2: Determine the load on an internal column at the base level of a 15 storey high rise building. The columns are spaced at 20 ft on centers. The total loading on each floor (dead + live) may be taken as 200 lbs/sq ft and the total loading on the roof (dead + snow) may be assumed as 100 lbs/sq ft.

Ans: See Example 5.11.2 in Chapter 5.

Example 3: A high rise rigid frame structure in Oklahoma is shown in Fig. 128. The frames are spaced at 22 ft on centers and the storey height is 12 ft. If all the wind is assumed to be acting on the windward side, with a total $C_D = 1.3$, show that the wind load is about 8 K at any intermediate storey level and about 4 K at the roof level, of an internal frame. The wind pressure at 30 ft height may be assumed as acting over the entire height of the building.

Example 4: A retaining wall 20 ft high is required to retain dry loose gravel (soil pressure 30 lbs/sq ft per ft of depth). The water drainage is good. Determine the total load per ft of wall causing the wall to slide.

Ans: 6000 lbs.

Chapter 3

LOAD PROPAGATION

3.1 Complex load paths

It has been seen that the loads that act on the structure find their way through the structural system to the foundations. This applies to both gravity loads such as dead, live or snow which are vertical or to wind loads which are horizontal. The behavior of the structural system in fact defines the path of the load. Alternatively, determining the correct load path leads to a correct appreciation of the behavior of the structural system. Sometimes there can be a number of alternative load paths. In such cases in structures, the shortest path is not necessarily the correct one and it is here that a complex analysis may become necessary to determine it.

Consider for instance, two beams **AB** and **CD** interconnected at their centers **O** and forming an elementary grid structure as shown in Fig. 18. The grid is acted upon by a load of **W** lbs which is say, the weight of a massive chandelier suspended from the point of interconnection. The beams are supported at their ends on columns which carry the load to the foundations and into the soil. The load of the chandelier is transferred upwards, as we have seen, through the mechanism of tension in the cable or chain, to

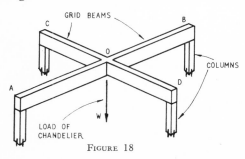

FIGURE 18

the point **O** of interconnection of the beams. At this point, the load splits into two components since there are two load paths through the two beams. Each beam then transfers its share of the load, through the mechanisms of bending moment and shear force, to the columns which then transmit it through the mechanism of compression to the foundation and hence to the soil. But in what proportion will the load split itself into the two beams at the point **O**? A wrong estimation of the share of the load in each beam would lead to an erroneous design of both beams causing one to be over-designed and hence wasteful and the other to be underdesigned and hence unsafe! For proper design, not only of the beams but of the columns as well, the exact load in the two paths must be determined. In this case, the answer to the problem lies in the fact that since both beams are intercon-nected at **O,** the load must necessarily split itself between the two beams in that proportion which causes both beams to deflect by the same amount. A study of **deflections** hence becomes essential to the analysis of the structure. This study of deflections will be considered in the design of beams in 5.9.

It is therefore clear that a proper appreciation of the behavior of a struc-tural system, so essential to its proper design, requires a correct understanding of the mechanisms or methods of load propagation such as tension, compres-sion, bending, shear and torsion for simple systems and an additional ele-mentary knowledge of at least deflections for somewhat more complex systems.

3.2 Tension

Tension is one of the most elementary mechanisms or methods by which load propagation takes place. Consider the chandelier shown in Fig. 4, whose weight is say **W** lbs. The load on the cable is hence **W** lbs. The cable can then be separated from the rest of the structure as shown in Fig. 19.

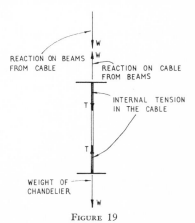

FIGURE 19

It is under an internal tension **T** whose value is **W** lbs. If the weight of the chandelier was 100 lbs, the tension in the cable would also be 100 lbs. The cable then transfers the load at its upper end to the underside of the beam. The load through the mechanism of tension in the cable has then reached the bottom of the beam.

3.3 Compression

Consider the four short timber posts or columns which support the carport roof, Example 2.9.2 and shown in Fig. 16. The load on each post or column tends to compress the post as shown in Fig. 20. If the load on

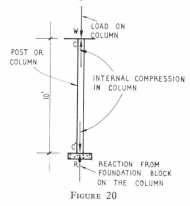

FIGURE 20

the column is **W** lbs, the column is under an internal compression of **W** lbs. The column then loads on to the concrete foundation block which then in turn loads on to the soil and attempts to compress it.

If the load on the column is 2943 lbs (as in Example 2.9.2) then the compressive force in the column at the top is 2943 lbs whereas the compressive force in the column at the bottom is,

C′ = 2943 + 90 (weight of the post or column itself) = 3033 lbs.

It is usual to design the post for **C′** as if it were acting over the entire length of the post.

The load through the mechanism of compression in the column has now reached the foundation block and thence the soil.

3.4 Bending moment and shear force

It has been seen that loads are forces and that forces can act at various points of the structure and in various directions. These forces can be transmitted through the structure by tension or compression when they act along the line of the structural member itself. When the loads act at right angles or transverse to the structural member, they are transmitted to the supports by bending moment and shear force.

In order to understand bending moment consider the action of a force **F** at the free end **B** of a bar of length **L** which is clamped at one end **A,** as shown in Fig. 21. Such a bar or member is called a **cantilever.** Consider

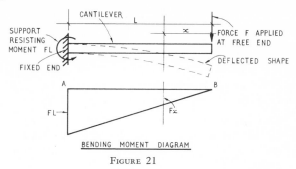

FIGURE 21

any section at a distance of **x** from **B.** This section has a tendency to rotate because the force **F** is at a lever arm distance **x** away from it. The moment of the force at the section, or the bending moment, is **Fx.** It is the force $\times$ the lever arm distance at which the force acts.

The moment of the force **F** quite naturally has the maximum value **FL** at the fixed end where the lever arm is the greatest. The bending moment at every section can be obtained and can be plotted as shown in Fig. 21. It is zero at **B** where the lever arm is zero and increases linearly to **FL** at **A.** This bending moment causes the bar to **flex** as shown in an exaggerated manner in Fig. 21, and so the bending action is also termed as **flexure.**

To understand shear force, consider the same cantilever with the force **F** applied at the tip **B** and shown in Fig. 22. Consider the cantilever material to be composed of a number of infinitesimally small blocks glued together as shown in Fig. 22. The force **F** attempts to cause the first block **P** to move or shear against the adjoining block **Q** at the common interface **XX.** The block **Q** attempts to support the block **P** at **XX.** The force attempting to cause this shearing action is **F** and so the value of the shear force at the

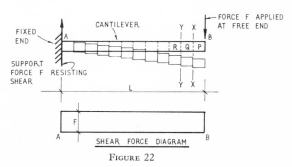

FIGURE 22

section is **F**. The blocks **P** and **Q** now together attempt to shear against the block **R** at the interface **YY** and the value of the shear force is still **F**. It can be readily seen that all sections of the cantilever are under a shear force **F** and the shear force diagram is hence a rectangle as shown in Fig. 22.

It can be seen in Figs. 21 and 22 that the load **F** at the tip of the canti- lever has been transmitted by the mechanisms of bending moment and shear force to the support at **A** which has to resist a bending moment **FL** and a shear force **F**.

3.5 Torsion

Torsion is another of the methods by which load can be propagated or transmitted towards the supports. Consider the tube **AB** shown in Fig. 23,

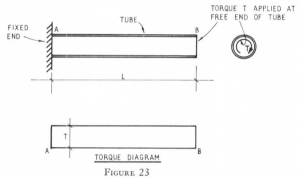

FIGURE 23

subjected to a torque (or twisting moment) **T** at the free end **B**. The tube is clamped at the end **A**. Under the action of the torque **T**, the tube twists, transferring the torque along its length until it reaches the support at **A**. Every section of the tube is under the torque **T** and so the torque diagram for the tube is the simple rectangle shown in Fig. 23. Torsion creates a shear stress in the material of the tube. This is because every section of the tube attempts to shear (in a circular manner) across the face of every adjoining section.

Torsion is a rather inefficient way of transferring load and should be avoided. In many situations it may in fact exist but can be neglected by the Architect. Consider for instance, the simple grid structure, with rigid joints of interconnection, as shown in Fig. 24 in section. Under the load- ing, the grid deflects as shown in Fig. 24. If the joints remain rigid, it follows that the slope of the beam **AB** at the points of rigid interconnection must be equal to the twist of the cross members. The cross member at **D** has no twist because the slope of the beam **AB** at **D** is zero. The cross members at **C** and **E** must twist however, because the beam **AB** has slope at **C** and **E**. The cross members at **C** and **E** are therefore under some torsion, but this is minor and can be neglected.

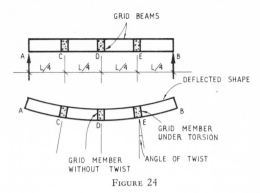

FIGURE 24

In some cases however, torsion is one of the primary mechanisms of load transfer. An example is the balcony bow girder of a theater. In such a case, torsion cannot be neglected in the analysis and design of the bow girder. Another example is the action of the wind on a vertical cantilevered sign post for a gas station or supermarket, as shown in Fig. 25. The wind force

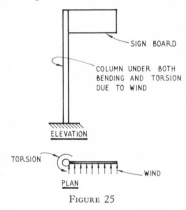

FIGURE 25

on the sign causes the cantilever to both bend and twist and both these actions must be taken into account in the design of the post.

3.6 Statics

It has been seen that the structure is acted upon by loads (such as dead, live, snow, wind, etc) and that these loads are forces which the structure attempts to transmit to the foundations or supports. This load propagation through the structure takes place with the help of the various methods or mechanisms of load transfer such as tension, compression, bending and shear, etc. The various individual elements of the structural system are hence under internal tension, compression, bending moment and shear force or combinations of these. Determining the values of the internal forces or moments generated by the load, in the various elements of the structure, by its passage through the structural system is termed as **analysis.** In the case of the cable supporting the chandelier, we determined the tensile force in the cable. That was analysis. In the case of the timber posts of the carport, we determined the compressive force in the posts. That was analysis. In the case of the cantilever, we determined the bending moment and shear force diagrams for the cantilever. That was also analysis. In the case of the tube we determined the torque diagram. That too was analysis.

It becomes clear therefore that to analyse the structure it becomes necessary to have some knowledge of the way in which forces and moments act (and hence can be determined) on structures in **equilibrium.** This is termed as **statics.** The essence of the problem is the analysis of structures in equilibrium. The Architect is however, concerned with structures which are not only in equilibrium but also at rest, since the structure, or part of it, can hardly take off like a car or a plane. This does simplify the problem conceptually, since the structure being at rest implies that the sum total, or overall **resultant** of all the forces or moments of the entire system over the structure or part of the structure must necessarily be zero. If the resultant force and moment were not to be zero, the structure would move under the action of the force and rotate under the action of the moment and for any structure that the Architect is concerned with, this does not occur. This overall equilibrium condition can be stated in the form of six equilibrium equations for displacement along and rotation about three rectangular coordinate axes **X, Y** and **Z** shown in Fig. 26. Since the structure is in equilibrium it cannot displace or move in the directions of the **X, Y** or **Z** axes and so the resultant forces along these three axes must be zero. This can be very simply written as,

$$\mathbf{F_X} = 0$$
$$\mathbf{F_Y} = 0 \ \dots\dots\dots\dots\dots\dots\dots\dots\dots\dots\dots\dots\dots\dots\dots\dots\dots\dots\dots\dots\dots\dots\dots\dots\dots\dots\dots\dots\dots\dots\dots\dots\dots\dots\dots\dots \ 3$$
$$\mathbf{F_Z} = 0$$

The structure or element of the structure cannot rotate about the three

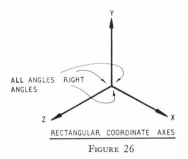

ALL ANGLES RIGHT ANGLES

RECTANGULAR COORDINATE AXES

FIGURE 26

axes either. This means that the resultant moments about each of these three axes must also be zero. This can be written as,

$$M_X = 0$$
$$M_Y = 0 \dots\dots\dots\dots\dots\dots\dots\dots\dots\dots\dots\dots\dots\dots\dots\dots\dots\dots\dots\dots\dots\dots\dots\dots\dots\dots\dots\dots\dots\dots 4$$
$$M_Z = 0$$

The above equilibrium equations are really all that are necessary for the analysis of simple structures. The equations of equilibrium can be applied either to the whole or to a part of the structure. If applied to the whole, the externally applied loads must equilibrate the external reactions of the supports on the structure. If applied to a part of the structure cut out from the whole, the forces and moments that exist at the cut must be reintroduced for equilibrium and treated as external loads. The part is still stable even when cut out from the structure because it was not the physical connection with the rest of the structure that kept it stable, but the forces and moments at that connection—which have been reintroduced. The part under consideration is then a **free body** which can be stable by itself. This concept of free body will be more readily understood in the analysis of trusses in 3.8.

It would be meaningless and a waste of time to study statics unless such a study is important to the analysis of structural systems. Whilst not all structural systems can be analysed only by the use of statics, there are some which can in fact readily be solved. Such systems are termed as **statically determinate** structural systems.

Statical determinacy is not unique to the structural system in general. In other words, the same structure say a truss, could be statically determinate or statically indeterminate depending on the support conditions and the nature of the joints. An understanding of the support conditions is particularly important to establishing the determinacy or indeterminacy of the structure and needs to be considered in greater detail.

The simplest type of support condition is the **roller** support as shown in Fig. 27a. This assumes that, for a vertical member, horizontal movement as also rotation is permitted at the end or support, but vertical movement is resisted. This implies that the horizontal force **H** as also the moment **M**

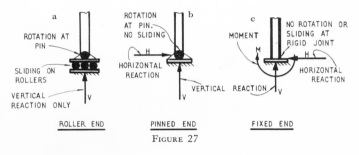

FIGURE 27

at the support must both be equal to zero. The only force at the support is the vertical force **V**.

The **pinned** end or support shown in Fig. 27b, permits rotation (as round a pin) but resists both horizontal and vertical movement. This means that both horizontal force **H** and vertical force **V** can exist but that the moment **M** is zero.

The third type of support is the **fixed** end or support as shown in Fig. 27c. Here both horizontal and vertical movement as also rotation are prevented. This means that all three quantities, **H, V** and **M** can exist as shown in Fig. 27c.

There can be other support conditions in between the cases considered such as for example **partial fixity** but these are specialised cases with which the Architect is not really concerned.

With appropriate support conditions, certain structural systems can be statically determinate and these are listed as follows:

1. Beam and post (column)
2. Pin connected trusses
3. Three pin arches
4. Some simple cable systems.

The analysis of these systems with the help of statics, to determine load propagation through the system and thereby defining its structural behavior, will now be considered in greater detail.

3.7 Beam and post (column)

This is a very simple structural system that has already been briefly examined in 1.6.1 where a statically determinate beam is simply supported on columns. The beam which is under bending moment and shear force, transfers the load as end reactions on to the columns and these end reactions are the loads on the columns. The columns under compression transfer the load to the foundations and into the soil. The example taken in 1.6.1 was a very simple one and beam and post systems in practice are more complex with perhaps a slab resting on secondary beams which load on to primary beams which are then supported on columns. The principle however is precisely the same. The structural systems of Examples 2.9.1 and 2.9.2 are beam and post. The best way to further understand such systems is by the help of simple practical examples which are considered below:

Example 3.7.1

Drawing the bending moment and shear force diagrams for the simply supported main beam of Example 2.9.1 and shown in Fig. 15. Determine also the load that this main beam transfers to the columns at **A** and **B**.

It was determined in Example 2.9.1 that the design load on the main beam **AB** was 800 lbs/ft. The span of the beam is 30 ft.

The total load on the beam is,

$$\mathbf{W} = \mathbf{wL} = 800 \times 30 = 24000 \text{ lbs.}$$

Let us use the simple principles of statics to analyse the beam.

Since the beam, now shown in Fig. 28, is in vertical equilibrium, it

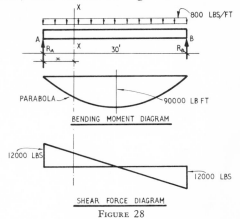

FIGURE 28

follows from Eqn. 3 that the sum of all the forces in the vertical direction must be zero. Therefore,

$$- \mathbf{wL} + \mathbf{R_A} + \mathbf{R_B} = 0$$

Upward forces have **arbitrarily** been considered as positive and downward forces as negative. The opposite sign convention if adopted, would also have been valid.

Now since the beam is symmetrically loaded, the reactions $\mathbf{R_A}$ and $\mathbf{R_B}$ must be equal since unequal reactions would destroy the symmetry.

$$\mathbf{R_A} = \mathbf{R_B} = \frac{\mathbf{wL}}{2} = 12000 \text{ lbs.}$$

The bending moment at any section **XX** at a distance **x** from **A** as shown in Fig. 28, can be obtained by taking the moments of all the forces that act on the portion of the beam to the left of **XX** about **XX** as,

$$\mathbf{BM_{XX}} = \mathbf{R_A(x)} - \mathbf{wx} \times \frac{\mathbf{x}}{2} \quad\quad\quad\quad 5$$

Clockwise moments have **arbitrarily** been considered as positive and anticlockwise as negative.

The values of the bending moment at various sections can now be readily determined by inserting different values of **x** in Eqn. 5 as follows:

When $\mathbf{x} = 0$ (at **A**), $\mathbf{BM} = 0$

When $x = \dfrac{L}{4}$ (at quarter span)

$$BM = \frac{wL}{2} \times \left(\frac{L}{4} \right) - w \times \left(\frac{L}{4} \right) \times \left(\frac{L}{8} \right)$$

$$= \frac{wL^2}{8} - \frac{wL^2}{32} = \frac{3wL^2}{32} \text{ lb ft.}$$

When $x = \dfrac{L}{2}$ (at mid-span)

$$BM = \frac{wL}{2} \times \left(\frac{L}{2} \right) - w \times \left(\frac{L}{2} \right) \times \left(\frac{L}{4} \right)$$

$$= \frac{wL^2}{4} - \frac{wL^2}{8} = \frac{wL^2}{8} \text{ lb ft.}$$

The bending moment diagram can now readily be plotted with the values of the bending moments as ordinates and is a parabola as shown in Fig. 28. The maximum ordinate at the center is $\dfrac{wL^2}{8}$.

For $w = 800$ lbs/ft and $L = 30$ ft we have,

$$BM_{max} = \frac{wL^2}{8} = \frac{800 \times 30 \times 30}{8} = 90000 \text{ lb ft.}$$

The shear force at the section **XX**, attempting to shear one side of the beam against the other side, can be determined by considering the vertical forces on the portion of the beam to the left of the section **XX**. The shear force can hence be got as,

$$SF = R_A - wx \dotfill 6$$

When $x = 0$ (at **A**), $SF = \dfrac{wL}{2} - 0 = \dfrac{wL}{2}$

When $x = \dfrac{L}{4}$ $\quad SF = \dfrac{wL}{2} - \dfrac{wL}{4} = \dfrac{wL}{4}$

When $x = \dfrac{L}{2}$ $\quad SF = \dfrac{wL}{2} - \dfrac{wL}{2} = 0$

The shear force diagram is a straight line diagram and is shown in Fig. 28. The maximum shear force occurs at the supports and is equal to the reaction of $\dfrac{wL}{2}$.

$$\text{SF}_{\max} = \frac{\text{wL}}{2} = 12000 \text{ lbs}$$

It may be observed from Fig. 28 that the maximum bending moment occurs where the shear force is zero.

The load that the main beam transfers to the columns at **A** and **B** is the reaction R_A and R_B. The load to each column is hence 12000 lbs.

Example 3.7.2

A simply supported beam is shown in Fig. 29. Draw the bending moment and shear force diagrams for the beam. Determine also the loads that the beam transfers to the columns at **A** and **E**.

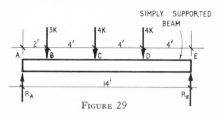

FIGURE 29

The beam **AE** in this case is not symmetrically loaded and so $\text{R}_\text{A} \neq \text{R}_\text{E}$. The beam however is in equilibrium and is not rotating about **A** or **E**. This means that, from Eqn. 4, the moment of all the forces acting on the beam about **A** or **E** must be zero. Taking moments about **E,** we have,

$$\text{R}_\text{A} \times 14 - 3 \times 12 - 4 \times 8 - 4 \times 4 = 0$$

$$\text{R}_\text{A} \times 14 = 36 + 32 + 16 = 84$$

$$\text{R}_\text{A} = \frac{84}{14} = 6 \text{ Kips}$$

It may be noted that in the above equations, the reaction at **E** has no moment about **E** because it passes through **E** and so its lever arm is zero. In order to determine R_E it is necessary to consider the vertical equilibrium of the beam. Since the beam is in vertical equilibrium, the sum of the vertical forces, by Eqn. 3, must be equal to zero. Hence,

$$\text{R}_\text{A} + \text{R}_\text{E} - 3 - 4 - 4 = 0$$

$$\text{R}_\text{A} + \text{R}_\text{E} = 11$$

$$\text{R}_\text{E} = 11 - \text{R}_\text{A} = 11 - 6 = 5 \text{ Kips.}$$

The bending moments can now be determined very easily using the same principles as in Example 3.7.1. It can be seen that R_A is the only force between **A** and **B.** The bending moment diagram between **A** and **B** must therefore be a straight line with a value at **A** of **BM** $= 0$ (**R$_A$** exists but has no lever arm) and a value at **B** of **BM** $=$ **R$_A$** $\times 2 = 12$ K ft.

The values of bending moments at other points can similarly be obtained as,

BM$_C$ $=$ **R$_A$** $\times 6 - 3 \times 4 = 6 \times 6 - 3 \times 4 = 24$ K ft.

BM$_D$ $=$ **R$_A$** $\times 10 - 3 \times 8 - 4 \times 4 = 60 - 24 - 16 = 20$ K ft.

BM$_E$ $=$ **R$_A$** $\times 14 - 3 \times 12 - 4 \times 8 - 4 \times 4 = 84 - 36 - 32 - 16 = 0$ K ft.

The bending moment diagram has been shown in Fig. 30.

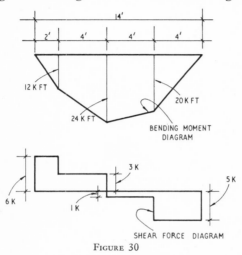

FIGURE 30

The shear force between **A** and **B** is the reaction at **A** $= 6$ Kips

The shear force between **B** and **C** is **R$_A$** acting up and 3 K acting down $= 6 - 3 = 3$ Kips.

The shear force between **C** and **D** $= 6 - 3 - 4 = -1$ Kip.

The shear force between **D** and **E** $= 6 - 3 - 4 - 4 = -5$ Kips.

The shear force diagram for the beam **AE** is shown in Fig. 30.

The load that the beam imposes on or transfers to the columns at **A** and **E** are,

Load on column at **A** $=$ **R$_A$** $= 6$ Kips

Load on column at **E** $=$ **R$_E$** $= 5$ Kips.

3.8 Pin connected trusses

Trusses are a type of structural system used for roofing large spans. They are more often used for roofs than for floors, because the structural depth taken up by a truss is fairly large. Some types of timber trusses are shown in Fig. 31. The average depth/span ratio for timber trusses other than pitched, for economical design, varies between $\frac{1}{8}$ and $\frac{1}{12}$ depending on the type of truss. This does not of course mean that timber trusses with depth/span ratios outside these limits cannot be built. They can be designed and built quite easily. Pitched trusses have a ratio $\frac{1}{6}$ and deeper.

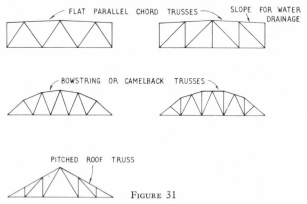

FIGURE 31

Some types of steel trusses are shown in Fig. 32. Steel trusses have generally lower depth/span ratios than timber trusses varying from $\frac{1}{10}$ to $\frac{1}{15}$. Pitched trusses again have a ratio $\frac{1}{6}$ and deeper.

If the joints of the truss are pin connected (or assumed to be so), if one end of the truss is on rollers (or a connection that permits small horizontal movement) and if the number of members used to form the truss results in

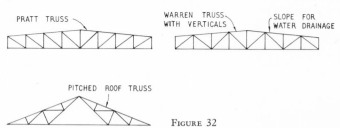

FIGURE 32

simple triangulation, as in all the types shown in Figs. 31 and 32, then the truss is statically determinate and can be analysed by the simple rules of statics. In practice however, the joints even if bolted or welded are assumed to be pin connected, the support conditions are assumed to have one end on rollers with the other end pinned and the truss is assumed to be statically determinate—provided it has the correct number of members to result in simple triangulation. In order to achieve this, the number of members **n** must be related to the number of joints **j** of the pin connected truss by the equation,

$$\mathbf{n} = 2\mathbf{j} - 3 \dotfill 7$$

If the number of members is more than obtained from Eqn. 7 (as by the provision of an extra diagonal), the truss is statically indeterminate. If the number of members is less than obtained from Eqn. 7 (as by the removal of a diagonal), the truss forms a mechanism and will collapse!

In order to understand the structural behavior of trusses it is necessary to understand the manner in which load propagation takes place through the structural system.

Consider the pin connected truss shown in Fig. 33. The end **A** is pinned

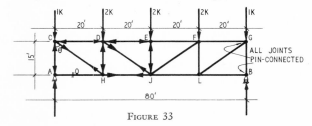

FIGURE 33

whilst the end **B** is on rollers. The number of members **n** is 17 whilst the number of joints **j** is 10.

$$17 = 2 \times 10 - 3$$

The Eqn. 7 is hence exactly satisfied and the truss is statically determinate.

In order to understand its structural behavior, it may be looked upon as a deep built up beam which under load deflects to the shape shown grossly exaggerated in Fig. 34. If the length of the neutral axis, in between

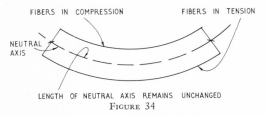

FIGURE 34

the upper chord and the lower chord, is assumed as unchanged, then it can be seen from a consideration of the lengths of the arcs involved, that the upper chord has to shorten and hence be in compression whilst the lower chord has to elongate and hence be in tension. The top chord of the truss shown in Fig. 33 is in compression and the arrows depict the members pushing outwards at the joints—as a compression member would do. The bottom chord of the truss shown in Fig. 33 is in tension (except for members **AH** and **LB** whose behavior will be considered later) and the arrows depict the member **HJ** pulling at the joints—as a tension member would do.

In order to understand the behavior of the verticals and the diagonals, consider two panels subjected to load as shown in Fig. 35. Since the load

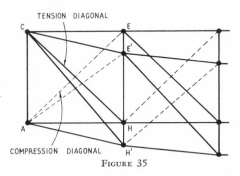

FIGURE 35

is on the top chord, the verticals have to transfer the load into the truss and to the bottom chord and so are in compression. The diagonal **CH** elongates to **CH'** and is hence in tension, whereas a diagonal **AE** (if it replaced **CH**) would shorten to **AE'** and would hence be in compression. For the loading shown therefore, diagonals in one direction are in tension and in the other direction would be in compression.

The overall behavior of the structural system is of course that it takes the load (assumed applied at the nodal points) with its members in either tension or compression, as we have seen, and transfers the load to its supports at **A** and **B**. The most efficient method of loading a truss is at the nodal points so that the members are only in tension or compression. This is not always possible however, and load may be applied sometimes directly to the top chord over its entire length. In that case, the top chord members, under bending moment and shear force, transfer the loading on the individual lengths to the nodal points, after which the system functions exactly as a truss as described above. The top compression chord then has to be designed for the compressive force as also for the bending moment and shear force that it carries.

In order to determine the actual forces in the members of the truss several methods can be used, the simplest of which is the method of joints considered in the example below:

Example 3.8.1

Determine the forces in the members of the pin connected truss shown in Fig. 33. Use the method of joints to analyse the truss. Determine also the reactions at **A** and **B**.

Consider the overall equilibrium of the truss under the external loads and the external reactions at **A** and **B**. The internal forces in the members do not enter into this calculation. Since **B** is on rollers, the reaction at **B** must be vertical. Taking moments about the pin at **A**, where no overall moment can exist, we have,

$$\mathbf{M_A} = 0$$
$$\mathbf{R_B} \times 80 - 1 \times 80 - 2 \times 60 - 2 \times 40 - 2 \times 20 = 0$$
$$\mathbf{R_B} \times 80 = 320$$
$$\mathbf{R_B} = 4 \text{ K}.$$

It may be noted that in the above calculation, the reaction at **A** and the 1 Kip load pass through **A** and so have no moment about **A**.

Taking vertical equilibrium of the truss as a whole,

$$\mathbf{R_A} + \mathbf{R_B} = 8 \text{ K}$$
$$\mathbf{R_A} = 8 - \mathbf{R_B} = 8 - 4 = 4 \text{ K}$$

Since the truss is symmetrical and the load is symmetrically placed on it, this could very well have been written down by inspection. In this example it has been proved that the reactions were equal and each had a value of half the loading. In all further examples the principles having been understood, inspection will be used where appropriate to determine the answer.

It now remains to determine the internal forces in the members of the truss. To do this we first isolate each joint as a **free body**. Consider the joint at **A** as shown in Fig. 36. It is acted upon by $\mathbf{R_A} = 4$ K upwards and forces in the cut members **AC** and **AH**. The forces in the cut members have to be replaced at the cuts so that the joint at **A** when removed from the truss is still in equilibrium. The unknown forces in the members themselves are very easily determined by taking vertical and horizontal equilibrium at the joint.

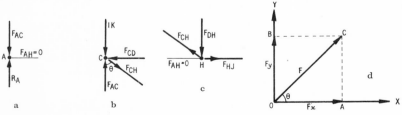

FIGURE 36

Taking vertical equilibrium at **A** we have,

$$\mathbf{R_A} - \mathbf{F_{AC}} = 0$$
$$\mathbf{F_{AC}} = \mathbf{R_A} = 4 \text{ K}$$

The force in **AC** has to push downwards at **A**. It must therefore push upwards at **C**. The force in the member **AC** is hence compressive.

Taking horizontal equilibrium at **A** we have,

$$\mathbf{F_{AH}} = 0$$

This illustrates an important principle of statics, that if three forces meet at a point and two of them are in the same straight line, then the third must be zero. The reason is that the third force, if it existed, would have an unbalanced component at right angles to the other two. Where as the two forces in the same straight line can balance each other for equilibrium, the third force cannot be balanced and if equilibrium is to be maintained, must necessarily be zero.

The analysis of the truss now proceeds by considering the equilibrium of the joint **C** after isolating it from the remainder of the truss as shown in Fig. 36b. The joint **C** is acted upon by $\mathbf{F_{AC}} = 4$ K acting upwards and the 1 K load acting downwards as known forces and by $\mathbf{F_{CH}}$ and $\mathbf{F_{CD}}$ which are the unknown forces in the cut bars **CH** and **CD**.

For vertical equilibrium we have,

$$\mathbf{F_{AC}} - 1 - \mathbf{F_{CH}} \, \mathbf{Cos} \, \theta = 0$$

The above equation illustrates another important principle of statics that an inclined force such as **F** shown in Fig. 36d, can be split into components at right angles and the vertical or horizontal component can be determined as **F** × Cosine of the angle that the force **F** makes with the direction along which the component is desired.

$$\mathbf{F_{CH}} \, \mathbf{Cos} \, \theta = 4 - 1 = 3$$

$$\mathbf{F_{CH}} = \frac{3}{15/25} = 3 \times \frac{25}{15} = 5 \, \text{K}$$

Since we assumed that the force in **CH** was tensile and the final answer has turned up with a positive sign, indicates that the assumption that was made was correct. If the force in **CH** had returned a negative sign, this would have indicated that the assumption made for the direction of the force was erroneous and needed to be changed. The force in **CH** is tensile and exerts a pull on the nodes at **C** and **H**.

For horizontal equilibrium,

$$\mathbf{F_{CH}} \, \mathbf{Cos} \, (90 - \theta) - \mathbf{F_{CD}} = 0$$

$$\mathbf{F_{CD}} = 5 \times \frac{20}{25} = 4 \, \text{K}$$

The force in the member **CD** was assumed to be compressive and the positive sign confirms that it is so.

The analysis of the remainder of the truss by the method of joints is given as a problem for solution at the end of this Chapter.

The truss can also be analysed and the forces in the members determined by graphical methods and as these methods often come easier to the Architect, they are of some importance. To understand such a method however, it is essential to understand a few basic principles governing the behavior of concurrent forces meeting at a point.

Consider two forces F_1 and F_2 meeting at O as shown in Fig. 37a. If

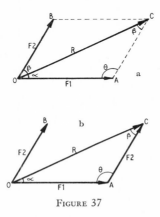

FIGURE 37

F_1 is drawn **to scale** and represented by **OA** and if F_2 is drawn to scale and represented by **OB,** then the resultant **R** of F_1 and F_2 can be determined by completing the parallelogram **OACB** and scaling off the diagonal **OC.** In other words, the resultant **R** represents the combined action of F_1 and F_2 acting simultaneously at **O.** The forces F_1 and F_2 can be replaced by the single force **R** acting alone on the body at **O.** A slightly different method of determining the resultant is to draw F_1 to scale and represented by **OA** and to then draw F_2 to scale and represented by **AC,** placed not at **O** but at **A.** The resultant **R** is then obtained by scaling off the third side of the triangle **OC** as shown in Fig. 37b. Whilst the first method is termed as

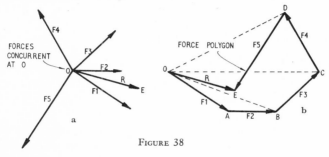

FIGURE 38

the parallelogram law and this method is termed as the triangular law, they are both basically the same since the third side of the triangle is also the diagonal of the parallelogram. The triangular law is very useful in statics since it can also be used to determine the resultant of a large number of concurrent forces as shown in Fig. 38. Consider the five forces concurrent at **O**. Then **F₁** is represented in magnitude and direction by **OA**. **AB** represents **F₂** and their resultant by the triangular law is given by **OB**, which can replace both **F₁** and **F₂**. **F₃** is represented by **BC** and so **OC** represents the resultant of **F₁**, **F₂** and **F₃**. The process can be repeated for **F₄** and **F₅** and the closing side of the **polygon of forces OE** is the resultant **R** of the entire force system. Quite obviously, if the polygon were to have closed with the concurrent forces themselves, would have implied that the resultant **R** was zero and that the concurrent forces were hence in equilibrium by themselves. Alternatively if the forces are in equilibrium, then the force polygon must be a closed one. It is really this little principle that is used for the analysis of trusses using graphical methods as will be seen by the example taken.

Example 3.8.2

Analyse the pin connected truss shown in Fig. 39a using a graphical method and determine the forces in all the members of the truss.

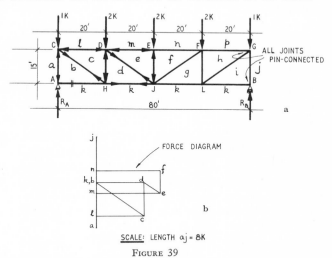

FIGURE 39

The truss shown in Fig. 39 is pinned at **A** and on rollers at **B.** The vertical reaction **R**_A and **R**_B can be determined by inspection as,

$$\mathbf{R}_A = \mathbf{R}_B = 4\,K$$

For the graphical method it is now necessary to name the spaces between the members as shown in Fig. 39a. The notation **ab** then denotes the member **AC.** The notation **em** then denotes the member **DE.**

Consider first the overall vertical equilibrium of the truss as a whole. Then draw **ak** which denotes $R_A = 4$ K **to scale** as in Fig. 39b. Going round the whole truss in an anti-clockwise manner, draw **kj** which denotes $R_B = 4$ K to scale and so on round the truss until **la** $= 1$ K downwards brings the line back to **a.** The truss is hence in vertical equilibrium since we started from **a** and closed at **a,** our polygon of forces in this case being merely a straight line.

In order to find the forces in the members at individual joints, all that is necessary is to consider the equilibrium of individual joints graphically.

Consider the joint at **A.**

Then **ak** has been drawn upwards vertically to represent R_A. Still in an anti-clockwise direction, from **k** draw a line **kb** parallel to **AH** horizontally. From **a** draw a line parallel to **AC** vertically. Quite obviously, the two lines meet only at **b** which in this particular case coincides with **k** as in Fig. 39b. **kb** has no length and to scale is therefore zero, whilst **ba** which completes the triangle of forces (in this case a straight line) must be 4 K to scale downward. The arrow at **A** is therefore downward, determining thereby that the force in **AC** is compressive. The arrow at **C** is therefore upwards.

Consider now the joint **C** and going again in an anti-clockwise manner, we have **la** $= 1$ K downwards and **ab** $= 4$ K upwards. The four forces meeting at **C** keep the joint in equilibrium and the polygon of forces must therefore close with the four forces themselves. From **b** draw a line **bc** parallel to **CH** and from **l** draw a line **lc** parallel to **CD**. The two lines meet at **c** to define the point **c** in Fig. 39b. The polygon of forces for joint **C** has now been completed and should be retraced for the arrows to determine the nature or signs of the forces. **la** is downward, **ab** is upward, **bc** is to the right so that the arrow at **C** for the member **CH** is to the right. This gives the force in member **CH** as tensile and can be scaled off from the force diagram as 5 K. Finally **cl** closes the force polygon at **l**. It is to the left from **c** to **l** and so the arrow at **C** for the member **CD** is to the left making the force in the member **CD** as compressive. The actual force in the member **CD** can be obtained by scaling off the length **cl** in the force diagram as 4 K.

The process can then be very easily repeated from joint to joint graphically to complete the force diagram as in Fig. 39b. The analysis of the remainder of the truss is given as a problem for solution at the end of this Chapter.

3.9 The three pin arch

The three pin arch is a very useful structural system in timber, steel or

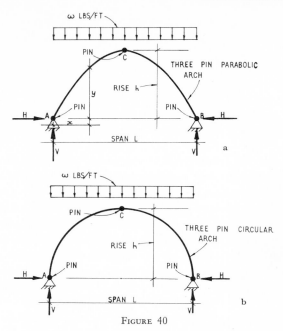

FIGURE 40

concrete for the roofing of large spans. It is characterised by the fact that it has three pins as shown in Fig. 40. If the shape of the arch is parabolic it is a three pin parabolic arch as in Fig. 40a. Fig. 40b shows a three pin circular arch. In both cases two of the pins are at the feet of the arch and the third pin is at the crown. Since a pin permits rotation and cannot carry any moment, as we have seen in Fig. 27, it follows that only axial and shear forces can be transmitted through the pins. This means that the sections at the pins can be theoretically smaller than other sections in the same arch that are required to carry bending moment. However for ease of fabrication and construction, the sections are often kept the same throughout the arch.

Arch action cannot develop, and the arch cannot behave as an arch, unless the feet of the arch are so anchored that the thrusts developed by the arch are capable of being resisted by the foundations. The pins at the feet of the arch transfer the axial thrust and the shear as vertical and horizontal forces to the foundations as shown in Fig. 40. The vertical force can be resisted by the vertical reaction of the soil, but the horizontal force cannot be easily resisted unless positive efforts are made to do so either by buttressing or by the provision of a tie as shown in Fig. 41. The horizontal tie can run below the floor slab as shown in Fig. 41 and need not interfere with internal circulation.

The structural behavior of a three pin arch and the load propagation

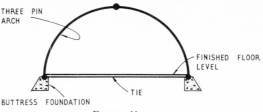

THREE PIN ARCH

FINISHED FLOOR LEVEL

TIE

BUTTRESS FOUNDATION

FIGURE 41

through it can now be considered. It is assumed that the foundations are such that the horizontal thrust can be resisted and arch action can develop.

The three pin parabolic arch is shown in Fig. 40a. It is loaded by a uniformly distributed load of **w** lbs/ft of horizontal span of the arch. It is pinned at the feet and at the crown. It has a span **L** and a rise of **h**. The rise/span ratio **h/L** is an important quantity for the overall dimensioning of three pin arches. If the ratio is very small (much less than ⅛) the arch is a very shallow arch and is not economical. If the ratio **h/L** is large, the arch is a deep arch and is much more stable. The **h/L** ratio varies from ⅛ to much greater than 1.

For vertical equilibrium, the sum of the vertical forces must be equal to zero.

$$\mathbf{V_A} + \mathbf{V_B} = \mathbf{wL}$$

Since the arch is symmetrical and is symmetrically loaded,

$$\mathbf{V_A} = \mathbf{V_B} = \mathbf{V} = \frac{\mathbf{wL}}{2} \quad\text{...} \quad 8$$

Consider now the equilibrium of one half of the arch. Since there is a pin at the crown **C,** it follows that the moment at the crown must be equal to zero. Taking moments of the left hand side of the arch about the crown we have,

$$\mathbf{V} \times \frac{\mathbf{L}}{2} - \mathbf{H} \times \mathbf{h} - \frac{\mathbf{wL}}{2} \times \frac{\mathbf{L}}{4} = 0$$

This gives $\mathbf{H} = \dfrac{\mathbf{wL^2}}{8\mathbf{h}}$ 9

The unknown quantities **V** and **H** have now been determined and the arch has been analysed. The bending moment at the pins is zero, but bending moment can exist at other sections in the general case and can be determined by taking moments about that section. In this particular case, of a uniformly distributed load on a parabolic arch, the moments are in fact zero all over the arch and the arch is subject to only axial forces which are compressive with complete absence of moments. This can be verified quite easily at some typical section say quarter span as follows:

The equation of the center line of the arch is given by,

$$y = 4h \left(\frac{x}{L} - \frac{x^2}{L^2} \right) \dotfill 10$$

where y is the rise of the arch at a distance x from A, as shown in Fig. 40a. The rise at quarter span when $x = \frac{L}{4}$ is,

$$y = 4h \left(\frac{1}{4} - \frac{1}{16} \right) = \frac{3}{4} h$$

The bending moment at quarter span is therefore,

$$BM = V \times \frac{L}{4} - H \times \frac{3}{4} h - w \times \frac{L}{4} \times \frac{L}{8}$$

Substituting the value of $H = \frac{wL^2}{8h}$ in the above equation we have,

$$BM = \frac{wL}{2} \times \frac{L}{4} - \frac{wL^2}{8h} \times \frac{3}{4} h - w \times \frac{L}{4} \times \frac{L}{8} = 0$$

Parabolic arches subjected to point loading and non-parabolic arches such as the circular arch will have bending moments between the pins. The load propagation in and the analysis of a three pin circular arch will be better understood by an example taken below.

Example 3.9.1

Determine the bending moment, shear force and axial force at quarter span for the three pin semi-circular arch shown in Fig. 40b.

In this case the arch has a span L and a rise $h = \frac{L}{2}$. It is loaded by a uniformly distributed load of w lbs/ft, as shown in Fig. 40b.

The horizontal thrust at the feet of the arch can be determined exactly as before by taking moments about the pin at the crown and equating to zero. This gives,

$$H = \frac{wL^2}{8h} \text{ and since } h = \frac{L}{2}$$

$$H = \frac{wL}{4}$$

In order to obtain the bending moment at quarter span it is necessary to determine the amount of rise that the arch has at quarter span where $x = \dfrac{L}{4}$. This can be determined very easily by considering the geometry of the arch as shown in Fig. 42.

$$R^2 = y^2 + \left(\frac{L}{2} - x \right)^2 \quad \text{..} \quad 11$$

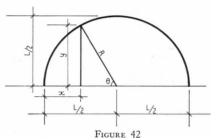

FIGURE 42

where $R = \dfrac{L}{2}$ and $x = \dfrac{L}{4}$. This gives,

$$\left(\frac{L}{2} \right)^2 = y^2 + \left(\frac{L}{4} \right)^2$$

$$y^2 = \frac{3L^2}{16}$$

$$y = 0.433L$$

The angle θ is also defined by

$$\mathbf{Cos}\ \theta = \frac{L/4}{L/2} = \frac{1}{2}$$

The angle θ is therefore 60°.

The bending moment at quarter span can now be determined as,

$$BM = Vx - Hy - wx\ \frac{x}{2}$$

$$BM = \frac{wL}{2} \times \frac{L}{4} - \frac{wL}{4} \times 0.433L - w \times \frac{L}{4} \times \frac{L}{8}$$

$$BM = 0.125\ wL^2 - 0.108\ wL^2 - 0.031\ wL^2$$

$$BM = -0.014\ wL^2$$

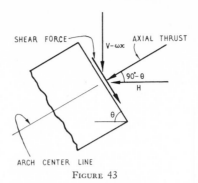

ARCH CENTER LINE
FIGURE 43

The shear force and the axial force at the quarter span can be determined by considering a cut section as shown in Fig. 43.

The shear force at the section can be got by taking components normal or at right angles to the arch center line. This gives,

$$\mathbf{SF} = -\,\mathbf{H\ Cos}\ 60° + (\mathbf{V} - \mathbf{wx})\ \mathbf{Cos}\ 30°$$

$$\mathbf{SF} = -\frac{\mathbf{wL}}{4} \times \frac{1}{2} + \left(\frac{\mathbf{wL}}{2} - \frac{\mathbf{wL}}{4} \right) \times \frac{\sqrt{3}}{2}$$

$$\mathbf{SF} = -\,0.125\ \mathbf{wL} + 0.216\ \mathbf{wL}$$

$$\mathbf{SF} = 0.091\ \mathbf{wL}$$

The axial force at quarter span can similarly be calculated by taking components along the arch center line as shown in Fig. 43.

$$\mathbf{Axial\ Force} = \mathbf{H\ Cos}\ 30° + (\mathbf{V} - \mathbf{wx})\ \mathbf{Cos}\ 60°$$

$$\mathbf{Axial\ Force} = \frac{\mathbf{wL}}{4} \times \frac{\sqrt{3}}{2} + \frac{\mathbf{wL}}{4} \times \frac{1}{2}$$

$$\mathbf{Axial\ Force} = 0.216\ \mathbf{wL} + 0.125\ \mathbf{wL}$$

$$\mathbf{Axial\ Force} = 0.341\ \mathbf{wL}$$

3.10 Cables

Cable structures are extremely complex structures which require very sophisticated methods of analysis for exact design. For an approximate design however, the analysis of cable structures can be considerably simplified and in some cases they can even be analysed by the simple rules of statics.

To analyse the cable however, it is very essential to understand its struc-

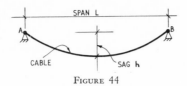

FIGURE 44

tural behavior and to appreciate load propagation through it. Consider a simple cable as shown in Fig. 44. The cable is suspended from its supports at **A** and **B** and has a span **L** and a sag **h**. The cable under its own load has the shape of a catenary which is only a little different from the parabola. Since the cable is a very flexible member, it cannot ever take any bending moment or compression. It can transmit force only in tension. Let this cable now be loaded by a load **W** as shown in Fig. 45. The cable then

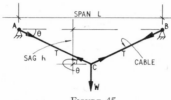

FIGURE 45

adjusts its shape or geometry so that it is still in tension. In other words it attempts to adjust its shape so that all its parts are always in tension under any conditions of loading. This fact enables us to determine the tension in the cable under the given loads. In the particular case considered of the cable subjected to the central point load shown in Fig. 45, the cable in order to stay in tension has two straight lengths **AC** and **CB**. The tension **T** in the two lengths can then be obtained by applying the simple rules of statics at the load point **C.**

For vertical equilibrium at **C**

$$2\,\mathbf{T} \times \mathbf{Sin}\,\theta = \mathbf{W}$$

$$\mathbf{T} = \frac{\mathbf{W}}{2\,\mathbf{Sin}\,\theta}$$

From the span **L** of the cable and the sag **h** of the cable, the length of the cable required can easily be determined as,

$$\mathbf{L_1} = \mathbf{L}\,\sqrt{1 + \frac{4\mathbf{h}^2}{\mathbf{L}^2}}$$

The ratio $\dfrac{\mathbf{h}}{\mathbf{L}}$ is the sag/span ratio for the cable. It is usually a minimum around $\dfrac{1}{10}$ for simple cables but can increase to $\dfrac{1}{2}$ or more for complex cable nets. The sag/span ratio is a very important quantity for cable structures and can affect the forces in the cables quite dramatically. Consider again the tension **T** in the single cable under the central point load as shown in Fig. 45. Then we have seen that,

$$T = \dfrac{W}{2 \, Sin \, \theta}$$

As the sag **h** is reduced, the sag/span ratio reduces as does θ. Hence **Sin** θ also reduces which means that the tension **T** in the cable increases. If the cable were to have no sag at all, then $\theta = 0$, **Sin** $\theta = 0$ and **T** would be infinite! The cable would then tear itself apart! A cable structure hence cannot possibly operate without a sag, however small it may be.

Example 3.10.1

Determine the tension in the cable shown in Fig. 45 under a central point load of 1 K. The span of the cable is 60 ft and the sag is 15 ft. Determine also the total length of the cable required.

For the problem,

$$W = 1 \, K$$
$$L = 60 \, ft$$
$$h = 15 \, ft$$

The length of a side **AC** can be obtained as,

$$\dfrac{L}{2} = \sqrt{30^2 + 15^2} = \sqrt{1125} = 33.54 \, ft$$

Therefore,

$$Sin \, \theta = \dfrac{15}{33.54} = 0.447$$

$$T = \dfrac{W}{2 \, Sin \, \theta} = \dfrac{1}{2 \times 0.447} = 1.12 \, K$$

The total length of the cable L_1 is $2 \times 33.54 = 67.08$ ft.

It has been seen that the cable adjusts its geometry so that it is always in tension under any conditions of loading. This fact can also be used to advantage in a graphical method when the cable is subjected to a large number of point loads. The method can best be explained by the help of an example.

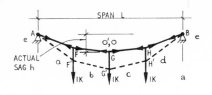

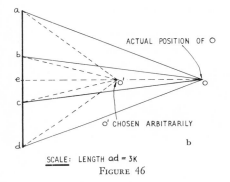

SCALE: LENGTH ad = 3K

FIGURE 46

Example 3.10.2

Determine the tensions in the cable shown in Fig. 46 when the span of the cable is 60 ft and the sag is 7.5 ft. It is symmetrically loaded with three 1 K loads as shown in Fig. 46.

The maximum sag is given as 7.5 ft and this is the sag at **G.** The cable takes a shape **AFGHB** such that all its parts are in tension. Whilst we do know the sag at **G** we do not know the sag at **F** and **H,** and if these were determined, the shape of the cable would be known and the tensions in the cable could then be easily determined. The problem therefore reduces to determining the sag at **F** and **H.** The graphical method can then be applied as follows:

The spaces between the forces are denoted by **a, b, c, d, e** and **o** precisely as in the truss problem of Example 3.8.2. The notation **ab** then denotes the force of 1 K which is the boundary of space **a** and space **b.** The notation **oa** denotes the tension in the cable length **AF.**

The overall vertical equilibrium of the cable can now be easily established also exactly as in the truss problem, by drawing the external forces to scale on a vertical line (because the forces are vertical) as shown in Fig. 46b. **ab** is 1 K to scale downward, **bc** is 1 K to scale downward, **cd** is 1 K to scale downward, **de** is 1½ K to scale upward and finally **ea** is 1½ K to scale upward. This closes the line at **a** thereby establishing that the resultant of all the external vertical forces and the external reactions is zero and that the cable is hence in vertical equilibrium. It may be noted here that the external vertical reactions at **A** and **B** were determined as 1½ K by inspection, as has been taught previously.

Now choose a point **o′ arbitrarily** on the line at right angles to **abcd** at **e** and connect **ao′, bo′, co′** and **do′**. Consider the equilibrium of the cable at **F** in precisely the same way in which the equilibrium of the individual joints was considered in the truss problem of Example 3.8.2. The joint **F** is in equilibrium under the 1 K load **ab** and the cable tensions **bo′** and **oa′** as in Fig. 46b. This means that the cable shape at **F** must be parallel to **ao′** and **bo′** since the tension in the cable can act only along the cable. The lines **AF′** and **F′G′** are hence drawn parallel to **ao′** and **bo′** respectively as shown by the heavy dotted lines in Fig. 46a. Similarly the equilibrium of the points **G** and **H** can be considered to complete the dotted shape of the cable **AF′G′H′B** as shown in Fig. 46b.

Now the point **o′** was chosen arbitrarily so the dotted shape of the cable is **not** the actual shape of the cable. The dotted shape does however determine, for the cable to be in equilibrium, the amount of sag that the cable must have at **F** and **H** in relation to the sag at **G**. In other words since we do know that the sag at **G** is 7.5 ft, it is possible to scale off the sag at **F** and **H** proportionately as,

$$\text{Sag at } \mathbf{F} \text{ and } \mathbf{H} = \frac{3}{4} \text{ sag at } \mathbf{G} = 5.625 \text{ ft.}$$

The exact shape of the cable under the given loads has now been determined and can be drawn **to scale** as **AFGHB** as shown in Fig. 46a.

As the shape of the cable is now known, the determination of the tensions in the cable can be carried out very easily. This can be done once again graphically by reversing the procedure and drawing **ao, bo, co** and **do** parallel to **AF, FG, GH** and **HB** to intersect in **o**. This in fact determines the actual position of **o** in the Fig. 46b. The tension in the cable length **AF** is the length of **ao** which can be scaled off from the force diagram of Fig. 46b. The tension in the cable length **FG** is the length of **bo** and so on. These tensions as determined from Fig. 46b are as follows:

Tension in **AF** = length of **ao** = 4.00 K
Tension in **FG** = length of **bo** = 3.75 K
Tension in **GH** = length of **co** = 3.75 K
Tension in **HB** = length of **do** = 4.00 K

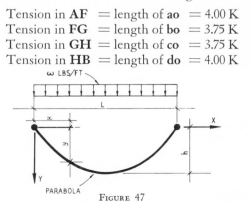

PARABOLA

FIGURE 47

As the number of loads increases, the geometry of the cable approaches closer to a smooth curve, until for a uniformly distributed load (on the horizontal span) the cable takes the shape of a parabola as shown in Fig. 47. The equation of the parabola is,

$$y = 4h \left(\frac{x}{L} - \frac{x^2}{L^2} \right)$$

It now becomes clear why the parabolic arch of 3.9 under uniformly distributed loading is in pure compression with complete absence of moments. It is merely an inverted cable which under uniformly distributed loading assumes a parabolic shape in order to be always in pure tension. For such a cable as shown in Fig. 47, the horizontal pull **H** at the supports and the vertical reaction **V** on the supports can be written as,

$$H = \frac{wL^2}{8h}$$

$$V = \frac{wL}{2}$$

The maximum tension **T** in the cable at the supports is therefore given by,

$$T = \sqrt{H^2 + V^2} = \sqrt{\left(\frac{wL^2}{8h} \right)^2 + \left(\frac{wL}{2} \right)^2}$$

3.11 Verbalising load propagation through the structural system

The understanding of a structural system is in reality an understanding of the manner in which load propagates through it. This can be done in analytical terms by analysing the forces and moments in various parts of the system thereby appreciating in detail its structural behavior. In many cases however, when an analytical approach may not be easily possible, it should at least be possible to **verbalise** the structural behavior of the system. This would result in a clear understanding of the manner in which load propagates through the various elements of the system and particularly the different mechanisms or methods of load transfer such as tension, compression, bending, shear or torsion that are used by the elements for propagating the load to the foundations. This would also enable the Architect to appreciate support or boundary conditions and hence also the supporting structure that he must provide if the system is to behave in the way that he wishes it to behave.

The capacity to verbalise structural systems is very important to the Architect and two simple examples are taken below.

Example 3.11.1

Verbalise the load propagation through the structural system shown in

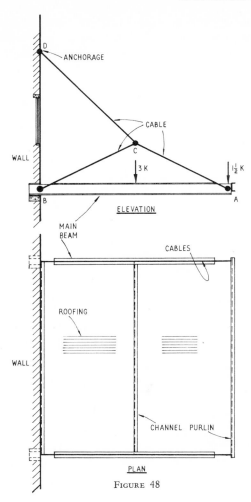

FIGURE 48

Fig. 48. Clearly outline the methods of load transfer used in each element. Comment on the support conditions and their specific requirements.

The structure in Fig. 48 is a roof canopy over an entrance. It is anchored into the wall structure of the building.

The member **AB** is a beam member with a 3 K central load and is simply supported by the pin support at **B** and by the cable at **A.** No fixity can be assumed for the beam in the wall at **B.** The beam is under a **bending moment** and **shear force** and transfers a load of 1½ K to the support at **B** and a load of 1½ K to the cable support at **A.** The load at **A** is therefore a total of 3 K acting vertically downwards and this causes a **tension** in the cable **AC** as also a **compression** in the member **AB.** The member **AB** has therefore both bending moment and shear force as a beam and compression as a strut. At the joint **C,** the cable **AC** then causes **tensions** in the cables **CB** and **CD** which transfer their forces to the supports at **B** and **D.**

The support conditions are shown as pinned at **B** and **D.** The pull of the cable **CD** along the line of **CD** will therefore attempt to draw the anchorage out of the wall at **D** and so adequate precautions should be taken to ensure that the cable is well anchored. The support at **B** will have both vertical and horizontal forces. The pull of the cable **CB** drawing the anchorage out of the wall is however balanced by the push of the compression member **AB** which tends to drive the anchorage at **B** back into the wall and so anchorage at **B** is not as serious a problem.

Example 3.11.2

Verbalise the structural behavior of the entire structural system shown in Fig. 49.

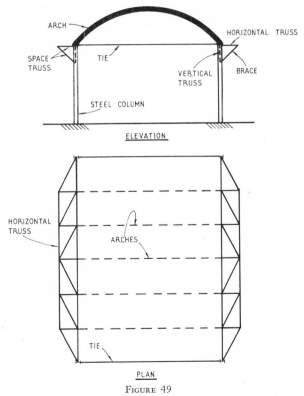

FIGURE 49

The structure shown in Fig. 49 is an arched roof structure set on four main columns. The circular arches transfer the load through **bending**

moment, shear force and **compressive axial force** in each arch to the pins at the feet of the arches. The load from the arch is transferred to its supporting structure in the form of vertical and horizontal reactions. The arches are supported on vertical trusses. Each truss takes the vertical reaction from the arches as loads and transfers them through **compressive** and **tensile axial forces** in its members to the columns on which it is supported at the two ends of the building. The horizontal thrusts of the arches have also to be taken by these trusses because it may not be feasible to provide horizontal tie members within the building. Since the vertical trusses are not capable of taking horizontal forces, horizontal trusses have also to be provided as shown in Fig. 49. Each horizontal truss takes the horizontal thrusts of the individual arches as loads and transfers them through **compressive** and **tensile axial forces** in its members to the columns at the two ends of the building.

The columns have therefore to take the vertical reactions from the vertical trusses and transfer them to the foundations. They do not need to take however, the horizontal reaction from the horizontal trusses because ties can be provided at the tops of the columns at the two ends of the building and this has been shown in Fig. 49. The ties in fact react the horizontal reaction of the truss on one side against the horizontal reaction of the truss from the other side.

Finally it should be noted that the weight of each horizontal truss has also to be taken by each vertical truss and bracing has to be provided for this load transfer. This in fact makes both vertical and horizontal truss as one three dimensional space truss, of triangular cross section, capable of taking both vertical and horizontal forces from the arches of the roof and transferring the load to the columns.

It may also be noted that the structural systems considered in Examples 3.11.1 and 3.11.2 were a combination of some of the elementary structural systems that have been considered earlier in this Chapter.

Problems for solution

Example 1: Determine the maximum design bending moment and shear force in the timber purlin and the glued laminated main beam of Example 2.9.2 and shown in Fig. 16.

Ans: Timber purlin, $BM_{max} = 2008$ lb ft, $SF_{max} = 502$ lbs
Main beam, $BM_{max} = 18366$ lb ft, $SF_{max} = 2671.5$ lbs

Example 2: Calculate the forces in all the members of the pin connected truss shown in Fig. 33. Use the method of joints. The problem has been commenced in Example 3.8.1. Check your answers against the values obtained by the graphical method in Example 3 below.

Example 3: Determine the forces in all the members of the same truss as in Example 2 above, but by the use of the graphical method.

Ans: The forces may be scaled off from the force diagram shown in Fig. 39b.

Example 4: A three pin circular arch is shown in Fig. 50. Calculate the horizontal thrust **H** at the feet of the arch. Determine also the bending moment, shear force and axial thrust at the 2 K load points.

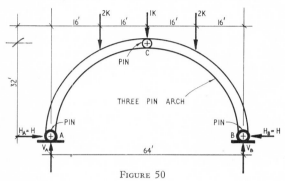

FIGURE 50

Ans: H = 2.5 K, BM = ~~29.25~~ K ft.

Example 5: Calculate the tensions T_1 and T_2 in the cable **ACDB** shown in Fig. 51. Span **L** = 60 ft, sag **h** = 15 ft, **W** = 1 K each.

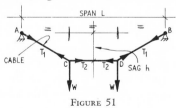

FIGURE 51

Ans: T_1 = 1.67 K, T_2 = 1.33 K.

Example 6: Verbalise the structural behavior of the system in the Architectural design arrived at in any of the more elementary studio design courses.

Chapter 4

MATERIALS OF CONSTRUCTION

4.1 Steel

Steel is one of the most useful of structural building materials. Because of its high strength it is particularly suitable for use with heavy loads and over long spans. The most commonly used all purpose steel is **A36** steel which has a yield strength of 36 ksi. In order to understand this, consider the stress/strain diagram for steel shown in Fig. 52. Such a diagram is

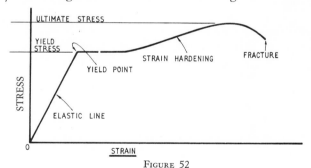

FIGURE 52

obtained by taking a laboratory specimen and subjecting it to a tensile force in a testing machine. The load on the specimen at various times and the elongation of the specimen at those times are noted. If the load on the specimen at some instant of time is **P** and if the cross sectional area of the specimen being tested is **A,** then **stress** on the specimen is defined as the load per unit area.

Stress $\sigma = \dfrac{P}{A}$ 12

The units of stress are lbs/sq in. or kips/sq in.

At that same instant in time, let the elongation of the specimen over a predetermined gage length of **L** be a small extension of $\delta\mathbf{L}$. Then the specimen has been strained and the amount of **strain** is defined as the change in length per unit length of the specimen.

$$\text{Strain } \epsilon = \frac{\delta\mathbf{L}}{\mathbf{L}} \quad\text{...} \quad 13$$

The units of strain are in./in. In other words strain has no units and is dimensionless.

If the stress at various times on the specimen is plotted against the corresponding strain, the plot that results is called the stress/strain diagram and for steel has been shown in Fig. 52. The stress increases linearly with strain up to a certain point (called the **yield point**) at which it yields suddenly with a large increase in strain at the same constant stress. This stress is called the **yield stress** and for A36 steel is 36 ksi. The slope of the stress/strain line up to the yield point is called the **modulus of elasticity** of the material and is a constant for the material.

$$\mathbf{E} = \frac{\text{stress}}{\text{strain}} = \frac{\sigma}{\epsilon} = \text{a constant value} \quad\text{...} \quad 14$$

The value of **E** for steel is 29×10^6 psi with a value of 30×10^6 psi being commonly used for design. Since the modulus of elasticity links the strain that the material will undergo under a given stress, with the material being used, it is in fact some measure of the deformation that the structure will undergo under the given loading. A material with a high modulus of elasticity, such as steel, will deform little under a given stress as compared to materials with a low modulus of elasticity, such as timber or plastics, which would deform considerably more under the same conditions. In shear, a shear modulus of rigidity **G** can similarly be defined. For steel $\mathbf{G} = 12 \times 10^6$ psi. In addition to A36 steel there are other high strength steels available for use by the designer. A572, A440 and A441 are high strength structural steels. A441 for instance, has a yield strength of 50 ksi. Its modulus of elasticity however, is still only 29×10^6 psi. This means that whilst the higher strengths may result in very slender and economical sections being needed to take the load, the deformations will be comparatively larger than for equivalent A36 steel members. So high strength steels are economical for members in pure tension and in situations such as short beams, where deflections are not critical, or short columns where buckling cannot occur.

The allowable or permissible stresses that can be used in design for A36 and A441 steels are shown in Table 4.1.1.

These steels are available in a variety of shapes such as I sections, channels, equal and unequal angles, hollow sections, etc., and these have been

Table 4.1.1
PERMISSIBLE STRESSES IN STRUCTURAL STEEL

ASTM Grade	Yield stress ksi	Permissible stress ksi			
		Tension	Compression (no buckling)	Bending	Shear
A36 36		22	22	24	14.5
A441 50		30	30	33	20

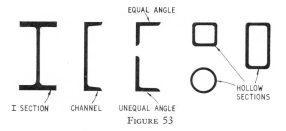

I SECTION   CHANNEL   UNEQUAL ANGLE
FIGURE 53

shown in Fig. 53. Each of these shapes has particular suitability for particular applications. I sections and channels are very useful as beams. I sections with broader flanges are used as columns. The angle sections are very useful in built up members such as trusses and for bracing where the leg of the angle is very convenient for bolting or welding to gusset plates. A joint of a roof truss using single angles is shown in Fig. 54. Since in the analysis of trusses we have seen that the members are assumed to meet at the nodal points, a little care in the alignment of the members and the detailing of the joint may be necessary to ensure that the assumption is justified. This is easily possible however, and is shown in Fig. 54. Finally, hollow sections are very useful as light columns for small loads.

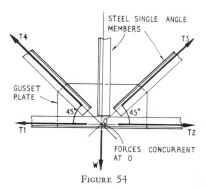

FIGURE 54

In addition to these shapes, steel is also available in the form of wires, ropes or cables for very high tensile strength applications. The allowable stress in such cables can be as high as 100,000 psi based on the actual area of the cable which is $\frac{2}{3}$ of its nominal area. The actual area is less than the nominal area because of the twisted strand construction of the cable.

Steel is also available in the form of rods for use as reinforcing bars in concrete construction. These rods called **rebars** have deformations on the surface to increase the bond between the concrete and the steel and range in sizes from $\frac{1}{4}$ in. to $2\frac{1}{4}$ in. In very thin concrete structures such as shells it is not very feasible to lay the small diameter bars individually and so a wire mesh can be used instead. This is a spot welded fabric of high strength wires in two directions. The fabric comes in a roll and is very convenient to place in the concrete forms.

4.2 Concrete

Concrete is a man made material created by the proper mixing together of coarse aggregate (such as gravel), fine aggregate (such as sand) and cement with adequate and controlled amounts of water. The cement forms a slurry with the water and under chemical action starts to set. The fine aggregate fills the interstices of the coarse aggregate and the slurry fills the interstices of the fine aggregate coating all the particles and binding the whole together into a monolithic mass when set. This is **concrete.** The complete curing for normal cement takes 28 days and so this period of time has to be allowed before load is allowed on to the structure. Sufficient strength is however developed for the formwork (in which the concrete was poured) to be struck in a few days. Rapid hardening cements are also available if the curing process has to be speeded up considerably.

Concrete is very strong in compression and ultimate strengths **fc′** of 5000 psi to 6000 psi can be obtained. The compressive strength of concrete however, can suffer large variations due to a variety of factors such as strength and quality of the aggregate, water/cement ratio, vibration or compaction in the formwork and proper curing. The allowable or permissible stresses in concrete for different values of the ultimate strength **fc′** for working stress design are shown in Table 4.2.1. Concrete is very weak in tension and so

Table 4.2.1
PERMISSIBLE STRESSES IN CONCRETE psi
Working stress design

Ultimate concrete strength fc′	Compressive stress in bending fc	Shear stress in beams vₑ
2500	1125	55
3000	1350	60
4000	1800	70
5000	2250	78

has to be adequately reinforced with steel rebars. The concrete then takes the compression with the steel taking all the tension. Both materials work together as a composite material. This material is then called **reinforced concrete.** A simple reinforced concrete beam is shown in Fig. 55. The

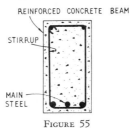

FIGURE 55

main steel is placed in the tension zone to take the tension that is developed whilst concrete in the compression zone takes all the compression. The shear force is taken partially by the concrete and partially by vertical stirrup reinforcement as shown. Two small diameter hanger bars are used in the compression zone to hold the stirrup reinforcement in place. Fig. 56a shows a square reinforced concrete tied column with the main longitudinal steel bars held together by lateral ties. Fig. 56b on the other hand, shows a round reinforced concrete column where the main longitudinal steel is held together by a spiral reinforcement. In all cases, the reinforcements form a

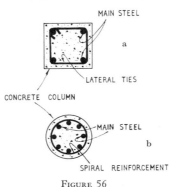

FIGURE 56

cage (horizontal for the beams and vertical for the columns) which are placed in the forms and then concreted. Since concrete is weak in tension, another approach to the problem is to **prestress** the element in compression so that the tension that would have developed in any zone under load is nullified by the compression already existing in that zone. This leaves the material, even under load, completely in compression and the concrete is then termed as **prestressed concrete.** The prestressing may be carried out either before the member is actually cast, in which case the prestressing strands are subject to **pre-tensioning,** or after the member is actually cast round the prestressing duct in which case the strands are subject to **post-tensioning.** In both pre-tensioning and post-tensioning, the prestressing strands that are used to provide the prestressing force are small diameter high tensile steel wires. These strands are about ¼ in. to ½ in. diameter with a very high ultimate tensile strength of 270,000 psi.

Whilst prestressed concrete can be poured in place and then prestressed, the great advantage of prestressed concrete lies in **precast** sections which are fully cured in the factory and then transported to site for easy erection. A large number of manufacturers manufacture a variety of shapes and cross sections for use as roof or floor members, columns and walls. One common type of slab for short spans is the **hollow core concrete slab** shown in Fig. 57. The hollow spaces can be readily used as ducts. The strength can be

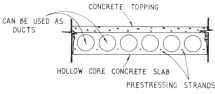

FIGURE 57

further increased by a normal weight or lightweight concrete topping which is poured in place and into which the electrical ducting can be set.

Another popular precast prestressed concrete section for rather larger spans is the **Double Tee** shown in Fig. 58. The spaces between the stems of the Double Tees can be closed in with ceiling panels and the spaces then used as ducts.

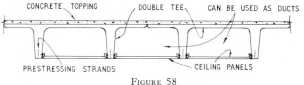

FIGURE 58

The **Single Tee** is suitable for even larger spans and is shown in Fig. 59. The choice and design of precast sections such as these will be considered in greater detail in Chapter 6.

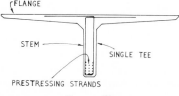

FIGURE 59

Precast sections are not used only for horizontal roof or floor elements. They can also be used as vertical elements for wall supports and for the cladding of the structure. Fig. 60a shows a Double Tee element when used as a wall panel. This may however lead to problems, if window openings are desired. In that case, a large number and variety of precast concrete wall panels with window openings are readily available. A typical panel is shown in Fig. 60b.

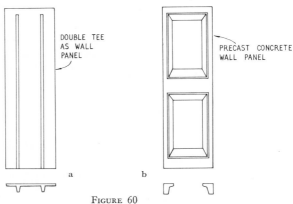

FIGURE 60

In all of the above cases, the manufacturer usually gives complete details of the connections that should be used between members. This is part of the service that the manufacturer offers to his client (the Architect) in an effort to encourage the use and hence the sales of his product.

Concrete is an excellent structural material which, since it is poured into forms, can be cast into a variety of shapes such as beams, columns, slabs, folded plates, singly and doubly curved shells, etc. Many very beautiful and devastatingly exciting structures have been possible only because of the superb flexibility of this man made material.

4.3 Timber

Timber or wood is a natural building material. It is available either as **lumber** which is natural wood or as **glued laminated timber.** This latter type is much stronger and consists of specially selected and prepared wood laminations securely bonded together with glue or adhesives. The laminations do not exceed 2 in. in thickness. Glued laminated beams are available in a variety of shapes and some of these have been shown in Fig. 61. Both lumber and glued laminated timber are widely used in building construction.

Wood contains certain natural defects such as knots, shakes, etc., and this requires that it be **stress graded** in order to establish design or allowable stress values for the particular member. Another factor that needs to be taken into account is the **grain** of the wood. The allowable stress in com-

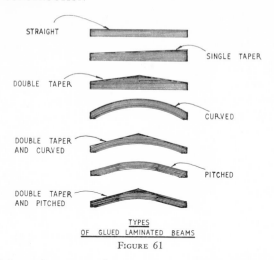

STRAIGHT

SINGLE TAPER

DOUBLE TAPER

CURVED

DOUBLE TAPER
AND CURVED

PITCHED

DOUBLE TAPER
AND PITCHED

TYPES
OF GLUED LAMINATED BEAMS

FIGURE 61

pression parallel to the grain, for instance, is higher than the allowable stress perpendicular to the grain.

The permissible stresses and the modulus of elasticity for oven dry, stress graded lumber and for structural glued laminated timber for **dry use** are shown in Tables 4.3.1 and 4.3.2. Dry use means that the moisture content in

Table 4.3.1
PERMISSIBLE STRESSES IN SAWN LUMBER psi

Type of wood	Bending stress f_b and tension parallel to grain	Horizontal shear	Compression	
			Perpendicular to the grain	Parallel to the grain
Douglas fir $E = 1.76 \times 10^6$ psi	1200-2050	95-125	390-455	1000-1800
Larch $E = 1.76 \times 10^6$ psi	1200-2050	95-125	390-455	1000-1800
Southern Pine $E = 1.76 \times 10^6$ psi	1200-3000	105-165	390-455	900-2200
Redwood $E = 1.32 \times 10^6$ psi	1300-1700	95-110	320	1100-1450

service is less than 16%. Wet use conditions, on the other hand, apply to exposed structures or to exteriors and to submerged structures. For wet use conditions, the permissible stresses are reduced and the reduction factors are shown in Table 4.3.3.

These tables apply only to **normal duration** of loading which implies

Table 4.3.2
PERMISSIBLE STRESSES IN GLUED LAMINATED TIMBER psi

Type of wood	Bending stress f_b and tension parallel to grain	Horizontal shear	Compression	
			Perpendicular to the grain	Parallel to the grain
Douglas fir $E = 1.8 \times 10^6$ psi	2000-2600	165	385-450	1500-2200
Larch $E = 1.8 \times 10^6$ psi	1900-2600	200	390-450	2000-2300
Southern Pine $E = 1.8 \times 10^6$ psi	1800-2600	200	385-450	1800-2000
Redwood $E = 1.3 \times 10^6$ psi	1400-2200	125	325	1800-2200

that the full design load is to act for a period of ten years. If the load is permanent, then a factor of 0.9 should be applied to the design stresses. For wind loads however, which are transient, a factor of 1.33 can be used.

Table 4.3.3
REDUCTION FACTORS FOR WET USE CONDITIONS

Bending stress f_b and tension parallel to grain	Horizontal shear	Compression		Modulus of Elasticity, E
		Perpendicular to the grain	Parallel to the grain	
1.00	1.00	0.67	0.90	0.90

This in fact permits a 33% overstress. The factors that have to be used to take the duration of loading into account are given in Table 4.3.4. They apply to both sawn lumber as also to structural glued laminated timber.

Table 4.3.4
DURATION OF LOADING FACTORS

Duration of loading	Factor
Permanent	0.90
Normal	1.00
2 months (snow)	1.15
Wind or earthquake	1.33
Impact	2.00

It can be seen therefore that accurate design in timber requires some information on the timber that will be used (Douglas Fir, Southern Pine, etc.) and the conditions of service likely to be encountered. Connections can also be important to proper design. A few typical connection details for

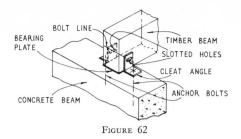

FIGURE 62

timber are shown in Figs. 62 to 66. These connections are shown here to demonstrate how the theoretical types of end conditions discussed in 3.6 and shown in Fig. 27 can be translated into practical connections.

Fig. 62 shows the connection at the end of a timber beam resting on a concrete beam. It is required to permit horizontal movement as in the theoretical roller support of Fig. 27a. This may be carried out in practice, as in this case, by the provision of slotted holes in the connecting cleat angles, as shown in Fig. 62. This permits the small horizontal movement that may be necessary.

Fig. 63 shows the manner in which a timber beam can be anchored into

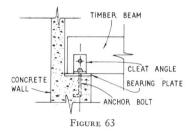

FIGURE 63

a concrete wall. The anchor bolts are set in the wall when the wall is being concreted. The timber beam can then be placed between the cleat angles and bolted through. The connection does not permit horizontal movement, but since only one bolt is used through the beam it would permit a small rotation making this connection of the pinned type shown theoretically in Fig. 27b. A more positive pin connection at the base of a timber arch is shown in Fig. 64. In this case the arch would have no difficulty in having

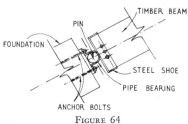

FIGURE 64

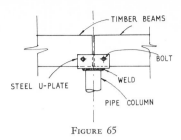

FIGURE 65

a small rotation about the base pin. A typical connection of two timber beams loading onto a pipe column is shown in Fig. 65. A steel U-strap is welded to the top of the steel pipe column and the timber beams then bolted through. The single bolts once again would make for pinned connections.

Fig. 66 shows a timber column bearing on a concrete wall. The anchor bolts are once again, set in the concrete when the wall is poured. The column is then placed between the cleat angles and bolted through. The use of two lines of bolts could make for a fixed connection of the type shown theoretically in Fig. 27c, but small rotations may perhaps be capable of occurring because of a lack of perfect fit and so this is really a case of partial fixity. The assumption that the column is pinned would be a safe assumption.

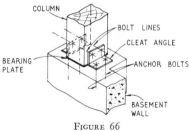

FIGURE 66

It should be clarified here that these connections are by no means exhaustive and that several alternative ways are available for timber connections. Nails, spikes, toothed rings, split rings, gusset plates, etc, are all useful connections for specific applications. Further information on timber connections is easily available from the manufacturers' literature on timber structures.

Another very important form of timber that is used in timber construction is **plywood**. Plywood is an engineering panel consisting of an odd number of veneer sheets placed crosswise to one another and bonded together under high pressure with an adhesive that is stronger than the wood itself. Plywood can be of various plies such as 3 ply, 5 ply, etc, depending on the thickness of the final sheet required. The permissible stresses in

Table 4.3.5
PERMISSIBLE STRESSES IN PLYWOOD (EXTERIOR GRADES) psi

Bending stress f_b	Tension parallel to face grain	Compression parallel to face grain	Shear	Modulus of Elasticity, E
2000	2000	1600	80	1.6×10^6 psi

plywood that can be used for Architectural design purposes are given in Table 4.3.5.

Plywood sheets can be used for a variety of purposes such as roof or wall sheathing. Their good racking resistance makes them particularly suitable as

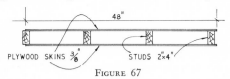

FIGURE 67

bracing panels. They can be used as the facing skins of complete wall panels as shown in Figs. 67 and 68. The plywood skins are glued to 2 in. × 4 in. timber studs, either on both sides as in Fig. 67, or only on one side as in Fig. 68.

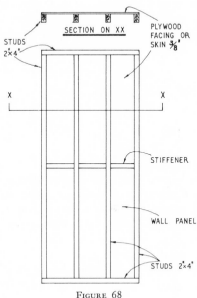

FIGURE 68

4.4 Aluminum

Aluminum is used in building applications for both structural and non-structural purposes. It has the advantage of light weight and superior corrosion resistance. This corrosion resistance is achieved because the aluminum forms a thin film of oxide coating on exposure to air, which prevents further corrosion. For even greater resistance it can be painted or anodised. Anodising is basically increasing this oxide film by electrolytic processes during which time various colors such as gold, bronze, grey, etc, can be given to the material.

Aluminum is too soft or ductile however, to be used by itself and so for building purposes it is alloyed with other materials mainly Magnesium and Silica. The two main alloys are 6061-T6 and 6062-T6. The permissible or allowable stresses in these alloys for purposes of design are given in Table 4.4.1.

Table 4.4.1
PERMISSIBLE STRESSES IN ALUMNIUM ALLOYS ksi

Tension	Compression (no buckling)	Bending	Shear	Modulus of Elasticity, E
19	19	19	12	10×10^6 psi

Aluminum alloy has one disadvantage in that welding is not recommended for connection between elements. Connections should therefore be bolted or riveted as far as possible. Sheets can be connected together by cleats or seams which can be locked together as shown in Fig. 69.

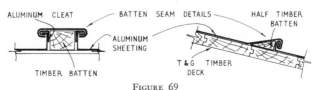

FIGURE 69

Aluminum alloy being a very ductile material is capable of being extruded into a very large number of shapes for particular specialised applications such as window framing, roof gutters, downspouts, fascias, beams, columns, etc. Three of these shapes are shown in Fig. 70. Fig. 70a shows an aluminum extruded beam section whilst Fig. 70b shows two simple aluminum extruded columns.

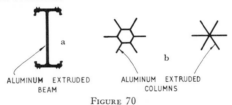

FIGURE 70

4.5 Structural plastics

Plastics are becoming increasingly important for both structural and non-structural uses in building. Their light weight (and hence high strength/weight ratios), superior corrosion resistance and excellent thermal insulation properties make them ideal materials for a number of building applications. Rain water goods such as gutters and downspouts are in PVC (polyvinylchloride), siding can be in FRP (fiberglass reinforced polyester) and counter tops are of melamine formaldehyde decorative laminates. The list is very large because there are a great many types of plastics available for specific applications. The reader is referred to the author's book **Structural Design with Plastics,** sponsored by the SPE (Society of Plastic Engineers) of the United States and published by Van Nostrand Reinhold Publishing Co., New York, for more complete information on the subject.

Basically however, plastics may be divided into thermoplastics and thermosetting materials. Thermoplastics such as acrylic sheet or pvc soften on the application of heat and harden when cooled. They are hence very suitable for mass produced items which utilise processes such as pressure injection molding or vacuum forming. Wire reinforced pvc however, can be used as the membrane of an inflatable structure. Thermosetting materials such as polyester or epoxy resins once cured, do not soften on the application of heat. They are hence more suitable for structural applications. They cannot however, be used by themselves and have to be reinforced with fibers—the commonest reinforcement being glass. This reinforcement can be in the form of a chopped strand mat, rovings or cloth.

The modulus of elasticity **E** of even the high strength plastics is very low, in the range of about $1 - 2 \times 10^6$ psi. This means that in order to overcome the large deflections that would result, the material should be used in those structural systems such as shells, folded plates, inflatables, etc, where deflections are not critical or where the structure has an inherent stiffness by virtue of its shape or form. The material is not suitable for use in conventional simple systems such as beams and columns.

Another important class of plastics are the low density materials such as expanded polystyrene or rigid polyurethane foam. These materials have a density of about $1 - 10$ lbs/cu ft, depending on the formulations. They are excellent for use as thermal insulation materials and as cores in sandwich construction. A typical sandwich panel is shown in Fig. 71. The facings can be in FRP or in aluminum.

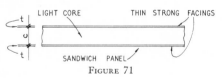

LIGHT CORE   THIN STRONG FACINGS

SANDWICH PANEL

FIGURE 71

Table 4.6.1
PERMISSIBLE COMPRESSIVE STRESS IN MASONRY psi

| | | Stone | | |
Brick	Hollow concrete block	Granite	Sandstone	Random Rubble
100-250	70-85	600-800	300-400	100-150

4.6 Masonry

Masonry can be of several types—brick masonry, stone masonry, hollow concrete block masonry, etc. Each type consists of the main block material (from which the masonry derives its name) bonded together by mortar. This mortar consists of a mixture of cement and sand which sets in the presence of water. The strength of the masonry hence depends partially on the strength of the brick or stone or block used in the masonry and partially on the mortar used in bonding.

The permisible compressive stress in various types of masonry is given in Table 4.6.1. Masonry is weak in tension and so no tension should be allowed to develop in it. This means that masonry has generally to be more massive than other types of construction to take into account small bending moments on the masonry and to guard against buckling. Masonry, except for special applications, does not really need to be designed since past experience, as laid down in the Codes or Manuals, dictates the thickness of masonry that needs to be used for common construction. Some such common rules for masonry can be easily referred to in Architectural Graphic Standards.

4.7 Soil

Soil is not strictly a structural material since structures are not built out of soil, except in the villages of severely underdeveloped countries—where mud is a structrual material in mud huts. Soil is however, always an engineering material since structures rest on soil and since, as we have seen, the loads must eventually be dissipated into the soil. The loads must be dissipated in such a manner as not to cause either soil failure or soil settlement and it is therefore very essential, for the design of the foundations, to have a good knowledge of the load bearing capacity of the soil. The load bearing capacity for various types of soils is shown in Table 4.7.1. Care must be taken in the use of these values, particularly for soils such as sand or clay which can be severly affected by the presence of water. The values can however be safely used by the Architect for his preliminary design. The Structural Engineer would need more information from borings or test pits to determine the exact nature of the soil for his final design.

Table 4.7.1
LOAD BEARING CAPACITY OF SOILS lbs/sq ft

Poor soil, with water Soft clay, silt, Fine sand	Average soil without water Medium clay, Compact fine sand, Loose gravel	Good soil, without water Hard clay, Compact gravel	Excellent soil All types of rock
1000	3000	8000-10000	15000 and up

4.8 Properties of sections

The various materials of construction have now been briefly examined. The materials are available in various shapes or forms. It is easy to see that irrespective of the material, the shape or section in which it is used, say an I section or a rectangular section, itself has certain properties which will influence the stress distribution in it. Knowledge of these properties is important to proper design since a more efficient and suitable shape of member would result in a lighter section for the same load and hence to a more economical design. Some properties of sections in general will now be considered in greater detail.

4.8.1 Cross sectional area

The cross sectional area of any section is easy to understand. It is the area of the cross section in sq in. and is therefore a measure of the total amount of material that is being used for the member. The cross sectional areas for some common shapes are given below:

Circle, $A = \dfrac{\pi d^2}{4}$, where d is the diameter of the circle.

Rectangle, $A = bh$, where b is the width and h is the depth of the section.

Triangle, $A = \frac{1}{2}bh$, where b is the base and h is the altitude of the triangle.

For more complex sections such as I sections, channels, angles, etc, the values may be obtained from the relevant handbooks such as the **Manual of Steel Construction** published by the American Institute of Steel Construction (AISC).

4.8.2 Centroid of the area

Any area has a representative point, representing the whole area, through which the entire area may be assumed to be acting. This point is termed as the **centroid** of the area. For instance, the centroid of a circular area is at the center of the circle. The entire weight of the circular area could be perfectly balanced by supporting it at the center. The centroids of complex shapes can also be obtained from the Handbooks.

4.8.3 **Second moment of area**

This quantity is also often referred to as the **moment of inertia** of the section, with the notation **I** being commonly used to denote it. This quantity is a measure of the way in which the material is distributed about the centroidal axes. As its name implies, it is the second moment of the individual areas about the centroidal axis being considered. Consider a small element of the area **dA** and let its distance from the centroidal axis being considered be **y.** Then,

$$\text{Second moment of the small element of area} = \mathbf{dA} \times \mathbf{y}^2$$

If all such quantities for all such small areas, in the total area, were calculated and summed up, the result would be the value of **I.**

Consider the rectangular section shown in Fig. 72. The area has two

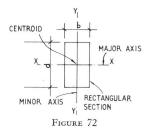

FIGURE 72

centroidal axes, depending on the direction of bending. These are **XX** the major axis and **YY** the minor axis and they are so called because the value of **I** about the **XX** axis is much larger than the value of **I** about the **YY** axis. These values are,

$$\mathbf{I_{xx}} = \frac{\mathbf{bd}^3}{12}$$

$$\mathbf{I_{yy}} = \frac{\mathbf{db}^3}{12}$$

15

It can be seen that the value of **I** can be increased quite considerably by increasing the depth of the section. In other words, a deeper section has a much greater **I** value than a shallow section—for the same cross sectional area. It is easy to see now why the same rectangular timber plank is much stiffer as a beam, and more difficult to bend, when placed on edge than when it is placed on its side. The larger the **I** value in the direction of bending, the stiffer is the beam.

The calculations of the second moment of area for complex sections have been fully determined and are readily available in the Handbooks. The AISC Manual of Steel Construction for instance, gives the **I** values about both axes, for every structural steel section available.

4.8.4 Radius of gyration

It has been seen that there are two quantities of importance—the cross sectional area **A** which gives the amount of material and the second moment of area **I** which is a measure of its distribution about the centroidal axis.

The radius of gyration **r** is an **imaginary** quantity that links these two values together in the relationship,

$$\mathbf{I} = \mathbf{A}\,r^2 \quad\text{...} \quad 16$$

We have, therefore,

$$r_{xx} = \sqrt{\frac{I_{xx}}{A}}$$

$$\text{...} \quad 17$$

$$r_{yy} = \sqrt{\frac{I_{yy}}{A}}$$

The radius of gyration is hence a simple imaginary quantity, with the dimension of length, associated with the section. Just as the centroid is an imaginary point at which the entire area could be assumed to be acting, the radius of gyration is an imaginary length at which the entire area of the section may be assumed to be concentrated to yield the same second moment of area as the actual section. As will be seen, this length is of great importance to concepts of column buckling, which are considered in Chapter 5.

4.9 Importance of the choice of the material to the Architectural Design

The choice of materials is a fundamental decision that affects not only the structural design but the architectural design itself. Certain structural systems and hence certain forms are more suited to particular materials than to others. A small doubly curved hyperbolic paraboloid (hypar) shell is appropriate in concrete, feasible in timber but a little out of place in steel. A clear and open span of 150 ft × 150 ft with a flat roof is possible economically with a steel or aluminum space deck.

It is not only in the choice of structural system that the material influences the architectural design. It is in the very appearance of the structure itself. Concrete construction is monolithic and gives an aesthetic effect of solidity, massiveness and a continuum form. Curves can be more easily emphasised in a concrete structure that is poured in place. Further the concrete itself can be left exposed and textured to further enhance any particular appeal that the Architect has in mind. If badly manufactured, it can also expose defects and blemishes in workmanship. On the other hand, timber blends in better with a natural rustic environment and steel can give a slender skeletal lightness to a deceptively strong structure. If badly designed, it can also become an engineering tangle of bars and joints. Vertical and horizontal lines can be strongly emphasised in a steel structure, since the material is available mainly in linear sections.

A proper choice of material can, whilst being rational and functional, considerably enhance the architectural appeal of the structure and not need any expensive masking to hide it.

Chapter 5

EFFECTS OF LOAD ON THE MATERIAL

5.1 Tension

Consider the example of the chandelier supported by the cable in tension as shown in Fig. 4. Then in 3.2 it has been seen that if the weight of the chandelier is **W** lbs the tension **T** in the cable is also **W** lbs. If the cross sectional area of the cable is **A** sq in., then it has been seen in 4.1 that the stress in the cable is the load per unit area given by Eqn. 12 as,

$$\text{stress } t = \frac{T}{A}$$

The tension **T** in the cable also causes the cable to stretch. If the actual stretch of the cable is δL and if the original length of the cable is **L**, then the strain of the cable has been defined in 4.1 as the change in length per unit length of the cable given by Eqn. 13 as,

$$\text{strain } \epsilon = \frac{\delta L}{L}$$

Let **E** be the modulus of elasticity of the material of the cable, then in 4.1 the value **E** has been defined in Eqn. 14 as,

$$E = \frac{\text{stress}}{\text{strain}} = \frac{t}{\epsilon} = \frac{T/A}{\delta L/L}$$

Rearranging the above equation gives,

$$\delta L = \frac{TL}{AE} \quad\quad\quad 18$$

The actual elongation of the cable can now be determined.

The effect of the load propagation through the cable has been to stress the cable with a tensile stress **t** and elongate it by an amount δL.

Example 5.1.1

Determine the tensile stress and the elongation of the member **CH** of the pin connected truss of Example 3.8.1 and shown in Fig. 33, when the load at the internal nodes is 10 K. The area of net cross section of the member is 1.25 sq in. $E = 30 \times 10^6$ psi.

The tensile force in the member **CH** was determined in Example 3.8.1 to be 5 K, when the load at an internal node was 2 K. When the load at each internal node is 10 K therefore, the tensile force in the member **CH** is 25 K. The net cross sectional area of the member is given as 1.25 sq in. Therefore tensile stress in **CH** is,

$$t = \frac{F_{CH}}{A} = \frac{25000}{1.25} = 20000 \text{ psi}$$

By Eqn. 18, the elongation of the member is,

$$\delta L = \frac{F_{CH}L}{AE} = \frac{25000 \times 25 \times 12}{1.25 \times 30 \times 10^6} = 0.2 \text{ in.}$$

It may be noted here that the original length of the member was 25 ft and has to be converted into inches for the calculations to be dimensionally correct.

5.2 Compression

Consider the carport roof of Example 2.9.2 and shown in Fig. 16. If the short timber columns are assumed to be in pure compression and no buckling can occur, then the compressive load in the columns is say **C** lbs. Compression is the exact opposite of tension and the Eqns. 12, 13, 14 and 18 developed apply to pure compression as well. We have therefore,

$$\text{stress } c = \frac{C}{A}$$

$$\text{strain } \epsilon = \frac{\delta L}{L}$$

$$E = \frac{\text{stress}}{\text{strain}} = \frac{c}{\epsilon}$$

$$\delta L = \frac{CL}{AE}$$

The effect of load propagation on the column, if in pure compression, has hence been fully determined. The effect of the load has been to stress the material of the column by a compressive stress **c** and to shorten it by a small amount δL.

Example 5.2.1

Determine the compressive stress in each timber column of the carport roof of Example 2.9.2 and shown in Fig. 16. Calculate also the elastic shortening of the column. Assume that no buckling can occur. **E** (for timber) $= 1.76 \times 10^6$ psi.

The total design load on each timber column (or post) was determined in Example 2.9.2 as 3033 lbs. The cross sectional area of the post was given as 6 in. $\times$ 6 in. $= 36$ sq in.

The compressive stress in each column is therefore,

$$\mathbf{c} = \frac{3033}{36} = 84.3 \text{ psi}$$

The elastic shortening of the 10 ft high posts is therefore,

$$\mathbf{\delta L} = \frac{\mathbf{CL}}{\mathbf{AE}} = \frac{3033 \times 10 \times 12}{36 \times 1.76 \times 10^6} = 0.00574 \text{ in.}$$

As may be readily seen, this compressive shortening is totally negligible and is never considered in design.

5.3 Buckling

If the column is short, the material is under pure compression and there is no possibility of buckling occurring. If however, the column is long and slender as shown in Fig. 73, the column will buckle long before the material crushes in pure compression—and at a much lower value of the load—causing failure of the column. The failure load for the column is then the buckling load, also termed as the critical load **Pcr.**

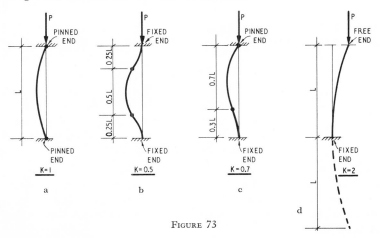

FIGURE 73

The value of the load **Pcr** at which buckling commences in the column depends on several factors such as the manner in which the load is applied, the length of the column, the shape of the cross section, the material of the column and the boundary conditions.

Consider the simple case of a circular long perfect column, pinned at both ends and subjected to an axial compressive load as shown in Fig. 73a. Then it can be shown (and the proof is not important) that,

$$Pcr = \frac{\pi^2 EI}{L^2} \hspace{6cm} 19$$

Where,   **E** = modulus of elasticity of the material
            I = second moment of area of the cross section
  and   **L** = length of the column.

The critical buckling stress **fcr** in the column is then,

$$fcr = \frac{Pcr}{A} \hspace{7cm} 20$$

The Eqn. 20 can be rewritten with the help of Eqn. 16 as,

$$Pcr = \frac{\pi^2 EI}{L^2} = \frac{\pi^2 EAr^2}{L^2} = \frac{\pi^2 EA}{\left(\dfrac{L}{r}\right)^2}$$

where **r** is the radius of gyration of the section.

The term $\dfrac{L}{r}$ is called the **slenderness** ratio of the column. It is a measure of how slender the column actually is for its length and cross section. If the slenderness ratio is very small, the column is a short column and the value of **fcr** as determined by Eqn. 20 may be larger than even that required to crush the material and so the material crushes long before the column buckles. On the other hand if the column is long and slender with a high slenderness ratio, the value of **fcr** as determined by Eqn. 20 is very small showing that the column will buckle long before the material crushes.

The column shown in Fig. 73a is pinned at both ends. Columns can have however, different boundary conditions and the critical buckling load for these different end conditions will now be discussed.

Consider the column shown in Fig. 73b. If the column is fixed at both ends, then the **equivalent** length of the column (between the imaginary pins shown in Fig. 73b) is only 0.5**L**. It is as if it were a column of only half its length but pinned at its ends. Substituting the equivalent length of 0.5**L** in the Eqn. 19 we have,

$$\text{Pcr} = \frac{\pi^2 EI}{(0.5L)^2} = \frac{4\pi^2 EI}{L^2}$$

The equivalent length of the column shown in Fig. 73c, fixed at one end and pinned at the other, is 0.7L. The critical buckling load can hence be determined as,

$$\text{Pcr} = \frac{\pi^2 EI}{(0.7L)^2} = \frac{2\pi^2 EI}{L^2}$$

The equivalent length of the column shown in Fig. 73d, fixed at one end but free at the other, is actually 2L, so we have,

$$\text{Pcr} = \frac{\pi^2 EI}{(2L)^2} = \frac{\pi^2 EI}{4L^2}$$

It may be observed that a column fixed at both ends is 4 times as strong as an equivalent pinned end column, whilst a column that is free to sway at one end is only $\frac{1}{4}$ as strong as it would have been if it had been pinned at both ends. The boundary conditions of the column are of great importance. Sometimes these boundary conditions are dictated by the manner in which the beams of the floor or the roof frame into the column. With a reasonably rigid roof or floor system, the columns may safely at least be assumed as pinned. With a very rigid foundation, such as a raft foundation, that is not capable of rotation, a column may even be assumed as fixed. In the absence of exact information on the conditions likely to prevail, the Architect must make a reasoned intelligent guess as to the boundary conditions that his columns have in his structure.

It should also be noted here that the value of I that has been used in the above equations is the minimum value. If the column is a round column, then the value of I about all axes is the same and the column therefore can buckle in any direction depending on defects in the material and small eccentricities of loading. If the column is an I section however, as shown in Fig. 74, the I_{yy} is less than I_{xx} and hence r_{yy} is less than r_{xx}. This means

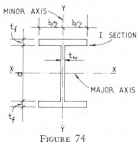

FIGURE 74

that the column will buckle about the **YY** axis since $\dfrac{L}{r_{yy}}$ is much greater

than $\dfrac{L}{r_{xx}}$. In other words, the column will buckle about that axis about

which it has a greater slenderness ratio and is hence more slender.

Example 5.3.1

An A36 standard weight steel pipe column has a nominal diameter of 6 in. and a length of 15 ft. If the ends of the pipe are assumed to be pinned, determine the ultimate load that the pipe can theoretically take before collapse. $E = 30 \times 10^6$ psi.

For the properties of the steel pipe, reference has to be made to the AISC Manual of Steel Construction. This gives the following information:

Outside diameter	$= 6.625$ in.
Inside diameter	$= 6.065$ in.
Thickness	$t = 0.280$ in.
Area of cross section	$\mathbf{A} = 5.581$ in.^{2}
Second moment of area	$\mathbf{I} = 28.14$ in.^{4}
Radius of gyration	$\mathbf{r} = 2.250$ in.

With pinned ends, the pipe can theoretically take,

$$\mathbf{Pcr} = \frac{\pi^2 \mathbf{EI}}{\mathbf{L}^2} = \frac{\pi^2 \times 30 \times 10^6 \times 28.14}{(15 \times 12)^2} = 257158 \text{ lbs.}$$

In a practical column, this load is never reached because defects in the material, eccentricities of loading, etc, cause the column to collapse at a much lower value of the load. This aspect together with considerations of the factor of safety will be considered in greater detail in 5.10 later in this Chapter.

5.4 Bending moment

The effects of bending moment on the material of the cross section can best be understood by reference to Fig. 34 in 3.8. The theory of bending is based on the assumption that the neutral axis of the section does not change in length. As the length of the arc reduces with a reducing radius, the fibers above the neutral axis have to shorten and are hence in compression. The amount of shortening that the fibers undergo increases with the distance from the neutral axis and the maximum compression hence occurs at the extreme fiber at the top. The same applies in reverse to the fibers below the neutral axis which have to elongate and are hence in tension.

The maximum tension occurs in the fiber that is farthest away from the neutral axis at the bottom. The strain distribution and the stress distribution across the section are both linear and have been shown in Fig. 75. It can be seen that the maximum stress occurs only at the outermost fibers at top and bottom, whereas all other fibers are understressed. It is therefore clear that an efficient cross section would concentrate as much material as possible at the extreme fibers where it would work at full stress. For this reason, the I section in steel is a very efficient section for a beam in bending since the heavy flanges are as far away from the neutral axis as possible and are held apart by a thin web. The rectangular section in timber is not very efficient for this reason.

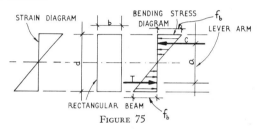

FIGURE 75

Consider the rectangular section shown in Fig. 75, subjected to a moment **M** which causes the stress distribution shown, which is triangular in both compression and tension. The stresses on the fibers can be summed up, to obtain the total internal forces **C** in compression and **T** in tension as,

$$\mathbf{C} = \mathbf{T} = \frac{1}{2}\,\mathbf{f_b}\,\frac{\mathbf{bd}}{2} \quad\text{..}\quad 21$$

where,

$$\mathbf{f_b} = \text{extreme fiber bending stress as shown in Fig. 75.}$$

These two forces **C** and **T** with a lever arm **a** between them, form an internal couple which balances the external moment **M** applied to the section. This keeps the section in equilibrium. We have therefore,

$$\mathbf{M} = \mathbf{Ca} = \mathbf{Ta} \quad\text{..}\quad 22$$

$$\mathbf{a} = \frac{2}{3}\,\frac{\mathbf{d}}{2} + \frac{2}{3}\,\frac{\mathbf{d}}{2} = \frac{2}{3}\,\mathbf{d}$$

Substituting the value of **C** or **T** as given by Eqn. 21 in Eqn. 22 gives,

$$\mathbf{M} = \frac{1}{2}\,\mathbf{f_b}\,\frac{\mathbf{bd}}{2}\,\frac{2}{3}\,\mathbf{d} = \mathbf{f_b}\,\frac{\mathbf{bd^2}}{6} \quad\text{..}\quad 23$$

There are two alternative ways of writing Eqn. 23. It can be written as,

$$M = f_b S \dots\dots\dots\dots\dots\dots\dots\dots\dots\dots\dots\dots\dots\dots\dots\dots\dots\dots\ 24$$

where **S** is called the **section modulus.** For a rectangular section as we have seen,

$$S = \frac{bd^2}{6}$$

The Eqn. 23 can also be written as,

$$M = f_b \frac{bd^3/12}{d/2} = f_b \frac{I}{c} \dots\dots\dots\dots\dots\dots\dots\dots\dots\dots\dots\ 25$$

where **I** is the second moment of area of the section as given in Eqn. 15, and **c** is the distance to the extreme fiber from the neutral axis.

Though the Eqns. 24 and 25 have been proved for rectangular sections, they are valid in general terms for other shapes as well. The section modulus for steel sections such as I sections, channels, etc, can be obtained from the AISC Manual of Steel Construction. The Eqn. 25 in its general form, holds good for unsymmetrical sections as well, though in this case there are two section moduli because the neutral axis is not symmetrically placed and there are two distances c_1 and c_2 to the extreme fibers. This has been shown for a Tee section in Fig. 76. Then,

$$M = f_{bc}\frac{I}{c_1} = f_{bc} S_c \text{ or } f_{bc} = \frac{M}{S_c}$$
$$\dots\dots\dots\dots\dots\dots\dots\dots\ 26$$
$$M = f_{bt}\frac{I}{c_2} = f_{bt} S_t \text{ or } f_{bt} = \frac{M}{S_t}$$

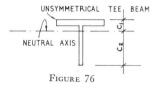

UNSYMMETRICAL TEE BEAM

NEUTRAL AXIS

FIGURE 76

The extreme fiber bending stresses f_{bc} in compression and f_{bt} in tension can be readily determined.

The above analysis shows that one half of the beam, in this case above the neutral axis, is in compression. We have also seen in 5.3 that members in compression have a tendency to buckle. For a beam in bending therefore, the compression flange has a tendency to buckle laterally, that is out of the plane of the beam as shown in Fig. 77. This can considerably reduce the carrying capacity of the beam. The lateral buckling should be prevented by providing lateral support to the compression flange along its entire length, as is provided to the secondary beams by the composite steel deck with

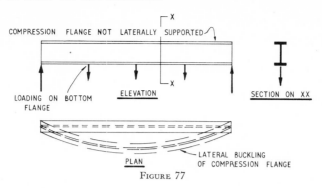

COMPRESSION FLANGE NOT LATERALLY SUPPORTED

ELEVATION

SECTION ON XX

LOADING ON BOTTOM FLANGE

LATERAL BUCKLING OF COMPRESSION FLANGE

PLAN

FIGURE 77

lightweight concrete topping as shown in Fig. 78. Since this is not always possible, it is quite acceptable to provide lateral support at closely spaced

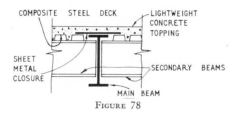

COMPOSITE STEEL DECK

LIGHTWEIGHT CONCRETE TOPPING

SHEET METAL CLOSURE

SECONDARY BEAMS

MAIN BEAM

FIGURE 78

points, as is provided to the main beam of Fig. 78 by the secondary beams which frame into it. If however, the compression flange cannot be given adequate lateral support, as for instance in the case of the underslung beam of Fig. 77, then either the load on the beam has to be reduced or a larger size of beam has to be provided to carry the same load. From the point of view of economics, this is naturally not very desirable.

Example 5.4.1

For the beam of Example 3.7.2 and shown in Fig. 29, it is proposed to use a W10 × 21 lbs/ft section. Determine the maximum bending stress in the beam assuming that the top compression flange is laterally supported.

The maximum bending moment for the beam was determined as 24 K ft in the Example 3.7.2. The relevant properties of the section can be obtained from the AISC Manual of Steel Construction as,

$$S = 21.5 \text{ in.}^3$$

Using Eqn. 24 we have therefore,

$$f_b = \frac{M}{S} = \frac{24000 \times 12}{21.5} = 13395 \text{ psi}$$

5.5 Shear force

The action of shear force in a beam has been seen in 3.4. The shear force tends to shear one section against another creating a shear stress. If the shear force is **V,** the **average** shear stress on the section f_s is obtained as,

$$f_s = \frac{V}{A} \quad\text{...} 27$$

where as before, **A** is the cross sectional area of the section.

This is the average shear stress on the section. The shear stress distribution however varies with the section. The vertical shear gives rise to a horizontal shear stress which causes horizontal layers to attempt to slip on one another. This horizontal shear stress increases with the depth or with a change of width. The parabolic shear stress distribution for a rectangular

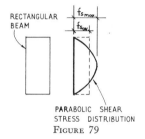

RECTANGULAR BEAM

$f_{s_{max}}$
$f_{s_{av}}$

PARABOLIC SHEAR
STRESS DISTRIBUTION
FIGURE 79

section is shown in Fig. 79. The maximum shear stress is hence higher than the average and can be got as,

$$f_s \text{ maximum} = 1.5 \times f_s \text{ average} = 1.5 \frac{V}{A} \quad\text{...} 28$$

For I sections, the shear stress distribution is as shown in Fig. 80. The sudden change in the width of the section at the junction of the web causes a sudden jump in the shear stress as the entire flange attempts to shear

$v = \dfrac{VQ}{Ib}$

I BEAM

SHEAR STRESS
IN WEB

SHEAR STRESS
IN FLANGE

FIGURE 80

horizontally against the web. The shear taken by the flanges is very small and so it is assumed that the shear is taken only by the web of the section. If A_w is the area of the web, the shear stress can be determined as,

$$f_s = \frac{V}{A_w} \hspace{5cm} 29$$

Example 5.5.1

For the beam of Example 3.7.2 and 5.4.1 determine the shear stress in the web.

The maximum shear force was determined in Example 3.7.2 as 6 K at the left hand end of the beam. The section chosen for the beam in Example 5.4.1 was W10 $\times$ 21 lbs/ft whose web dimensions can be obtained from the AISC Manual of Steel Construction as,

$$\text{depth of the web} = 9.22 \text{ in.}$$
$$\text{thickness of web} = 0.24 \text{ in.}$$

The area of the web A_w to resist shear is hence,

$$A_w = 9.22 \times 0.24 = 2.21 \text{ in.}^2$$

The shear stress in the web is therefore by Eqn. 29,

$$f_s = \frac{6000}{2.21} = 2715 \text{ psi.}$$

5.6 Torsion

The effect of torsion is to create shear stresses in the section as we have seen in 3.5. Consider the circular section shown in Fig. 81. Then the shear strain and the shear stress at fibers farther away from the axis of the section

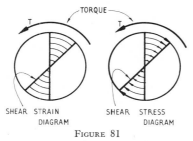

FIGURE 81

is greater than towards the center. The maximum strain and the maximum stress occur at the outermost fibers. The analogy can easily be drawn between the circular section under torsion and the beam in bending and we have,

$$M_t = f_s \frac{I_p}{R} \hspace{5cm} 30$$

where,

$\mathbf{M_t}$ = torque on the section,

$\mathbf{f_s}$ = maximum shear stress on the extreme fiber,

$\mathbf{R}$ = radius of the section and hence the distance to the extreme fiber,

$\mathbf{I_p}$ = **polar** moment of inertia, which is equivalent to the second moment of the area but for twisting, not bending, about the axis of the section.

It can be seen that, as in bending, the maximum stress occurs at the extreme fibers and so the most efficient section is the circular tube which concentrates all its area at the extreme fibers as far away from the center as possible. For a thin tube of thickness **t** and assuming that the shear stress $\mathbf{f_s}$ is constant over the thickness of the tube, the total force **F** that resists twisting can be obtained as,

$$\mathbf{F} = \mathbf{f_s}\, 2\pi\mathbf{Rt}$$

This force **F** acts in the thickness of the tube as shown in Fig. 82, at a

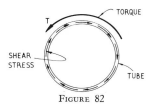

FIGURE 82

distance **R** from the center of the tube. The resistant torque is therefore,

$$\mathbf{M_t} = \mathbf{f_s}\, 2\pi\mathbf{Rt} \times \mathbf{R}$$

The shear stress in the tube $\mathbf{f_s}$ can hence be obtained as,

$$\mathbf{f_s} = \frac{\mathbf{M_t}}{2\pi\mathbf{R^2 t}} \quad\text{---}\quad 31$$

5.7 Design

The effect of load propagation, by the different methods of load transfer, on the structural element has now been considered and the member now needs to be sized so as to be safe and economical. This is design. This process however, since it involves the safety of the structure, is so important that various Codes have been written for the different materials to ensure that the member provided will adequately fulfil its purpose in the structure, with appropriate factors of safety. Steel design for instance, is governed by the Codes of the American Institute of Steel Construction as detailed in the AISC Manual of Steel Construction. Concrete design is governed by the Code of the American Concrete Institute ACI 318, whilst timber design is governed by the Codes of the American Institute of Timber Construction as detailed in the AITC Timber Construction Manual. These manuals must always be referred to for the trial designs and when in doubt.

All design basically involves first choosing a size or section and then checking to ensure that it is safe. If it is not, a larger size is chosen and the calculations rechecked. Design is hence a trial and error method of arriving at a safe and economical size.

The design of structural elements in steel, concrete and timber and based on the relevant Codes will now be briefly considered.

5.8 Design of tension members

The design of tension members is very simple. It is only required to ensure that the stress on the **net area** of the cross section provided (deducting for bolt holes, etc) is less than the tensile stress that is permissible for the particular material. The elongation of the member should also be checked. This applies to tension members in steel, timber or aluminum. The approach does not however, apply to tension members or ties in concrete. Concrete is very weak in tension and for such members the design is based on **all** the tension being taken **only** by the steel reinforcement. The concrete then merely holds the reinforcement together and provides any stiffness that might be necessary to prevent the rebars from sagging under their own weight.

Example 5.8.1

Design the tension diagonal **CH** of the pin connected truss of Example 5.1.1.

The tensile force in the diagonal **CH** was determined as 25 K. Choose a single angle 3 in. $\times$ 3 in. $\times$ ¼ in. thick. One of the legs will be attached to a gusset plate and will therefore have a bolt hole in it at one section. This is shown in Fig. 83.

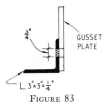

FIGURE 83

The gross area of the angle is 1.44 sq in., as determined from the AISC Manual of Steel Construction. Using ⅝ in. diameter bolts in ¾ in. diameter holes, the net area of the cross section can be got as,

$$\mathbf{A} = 1.44 - \tfrac{3}{4} \times \tfrac{1}{4} = 1.44 - 0.19 = 1.25 \text{ sq in.}$$

The tensile stress in the section is hence,

$$t = \frac{T}{A} = \frac{25000}{1.25} = 20000 \text{ psi}$$

The permissible tensile stress in axial tension for A36 steel is 22000 psi as given in Table 4.1.1. The section chosen is hence both safe (stress less than 22000 psi) and economical (stress near enough to 22000 psi). The angle is hence acceptable. Some Codes require that some part of the area of the outstanding leg be also deducted from the gross area of the angle to arrive at the net area, but for a preliminary design by the Architect this need not be considered. A little larger diameter bolt would also be preferable.

The elongation of the diagonal has been calculated in Example 5.1.1 and will not be repeated here.

Example 5.8.2

Design the cable of Example 4 in Problems for Solution at the end of Chapter 3, when the vertical load at each loading point is 16 K.

The cable is shown in Fig. 51. The maximum tension in the cable under a load of 1 K at each loading point is given in the answer to the problem as 1.67 K. Under a load of 16 K at each loading point therefore,

$$\mathbf{T} = 16 \times 1.67 = 26.72 \text{ K}$$

From 4.1 we have that the allowable stress on a high tensile steel cable is say 100,000 psi on the actual area of the cable, which is about $\frac{2}{3}$ of its nominal area. The actual area of the cable can hence be calculated as,

$$\mathbf{A} = \frac{26720}{100000} = 0.27 \text{ sq in.}$$

Nominal area of the cable $= \frac{3}{2} \times$ actual area $= 1.5 \times 0.27 = 0.405$ sq in.

The diameter of the cable can hence be calculated as,

$$\frac{\pi \mathbf{d}^2}{4} = 0.405$$

$$\mathbf{d}^2 = \frac{0.405 \times 4}{\pi} = 0.516 \text{ in.}^2$$

$$\mathbf{d} = \sqrt{0.516} = 0.72 \text{ in.}$$

Use a $\frac{3}{4}$ in. diameter cable. The total extension of the cable can also be very easily determined.

5.9 Design of beams

The design of beams is not very difficult. The three main factors that have to be checked and provided for are,

a. The maximum bending stress should be less than that permissible for the material.

b. The maximum shear stress should be less than that permissible for the material.

c. The deflection of the beam should be less than that permitted by the Building Codes.

It is in order to be able to take **c** above into account for the design of beams that it becomes necessary to now study the deflection of beams.

All beams under load deflect due to the bending moment and the shear force. The deflection due to shear is very small and can be neglected safely, except in the design of very deep beams or sandwich panels with light cores, when shear deflections begin to assume some importance. The deflection due to bending has however to be taken into account since large deflections can cause undesirable effects. The large deflections do not necessarily harm the member itself but they can cause glass panels, internal partitions and ceilings attached to the member to have large distortions and even cracking. In addition large deflections in a floor member might prove uncomfortable to the occupants of the building, whereas the same deflection in a roof member might not be objectionable. The allowable deflections are therefore dependent on the situation of the member, the use to which it is to be put and the attachments to it. These allowable deflections that the member can have as a maximum are laid down by the Codes and the rules governing allowable deflections are shown in Table 5.9.1 where **L** is the span of the member.

Table 5.9.1
PERMISSIBLE DEFLECTIONS

Type of member	Live load only	Total load (Dead load + Live load)
Roof members		
Without attached plaster ceiling	$\dfrac{L}{240}$	$\dfrac{L}{180}$
With attached plaster ceiling	$\dfrac{L}{360}$	$\dfrac{L}{240}$
Floor beams	$\dfrac{L}{360}$	$\dfrac{L}{240}$

It may be seen that the permissible deflection under live load only has to be much less than the permissible deflection under the total load of the dead + live load. The reason is that once the dead load comes onto the member and the deflection takes place, it does not change. Live load on the other hand comes on and off the member causing the member to move up and down. This fluctuating movement can be very damaging to the attachments.

Whilst the actual deflections are very small and hardly visible, in the case of very long spans where the deflections are likely to be unsightly, a camber can be given. This camber causes the member to initially have an upward deflection so that under load, the member returns to an almost horizontal position.

The rules that govern the amount of deflection that the member may be permitted, have been discussed. It now remains for us to be able to calculate the actual deflection that the member is going to have under the given loading and for the size chosen. If the actual deflection is less than the permissible, the section is acceptable. If the actual deflection of the member is more than that permitted by the Codes, then the size of the member should be increased and the calculations rechecked.

The actual deflection that the member will have depends on several factors such as the span of the member, the load on the member, the material of which the member is made, the second moment of area of the section chosen and finally the boundary conditions of the member. A simply supported beam will deflect more than an equivalent beam that is rigidly fixed at its ends. The actual deflection that any beam will have can therefore be written as,

$$\delta = C\,\frac{WL^3}{EI} \quad\text{..} \quad 32$$

where,

δ = maximum deflection of the beam

W = **total** load on the beam

L = span of the beam

E = modulus of elasticity of the material of the beam

I = second moment of area of the section of the beam, and

C = a constant which depends on the end conditions of the beam.

The value of the constant **C** for some simple beams is given in Fig. 84. It is not necessary to memorise these, or any other, values since the deflections of various types of beams under a variety of loadings are all easily available by quick reference to any good Structural Engineering Handbook.

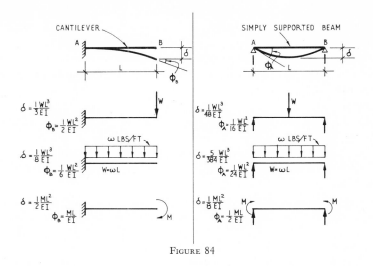

FIGURE 84

Example 5.9.1

Design the steel main beam of Example 3.7.1. Assume that the corridor is protected by a light steel railing whose weight can be neglected.

It was determined in Example 3.7.1 that the maximum bending moment on the beam is 90,000 lb ft and the maximum shear force is 12000 lbs. For A36 steel, the maximum permissible bending stress is 24000 psi, as given in Table 4.1.1. From Eqn. 24, the section modulus S that is required can be obtained as,

$$S = \frac{M}{f_b} = \frac{90000 \times 12}{24000} = 45 \text{ in.}^3$$

Try a W16 × 36 lbs/ft section. The properties of the section can be obtained from the AISC Manual of Steel Construction as,

depth $= 16$ in.
flange width $= 7$ in.
section modulus $S = 56.3$ in.^{3}
second moment of area $I = 446.3$ in.^{4}
depth of web $= 15$ in.
thickness of the web $= 0.30$ in.

The section chosen has a section modulus S of 56.3 in.^{3} and so is acceptable in bending.

The shear stress on the web will now be checked and we have,

Shear force on the beam $V = 12000$ lbs
Area of the web for shear $A_w = 15 \times 0.30 = 4.5$ sq in.

The shear stress $\mathbf{v}$ or $\mathbf{f_s}$ from Eqn. 29 can be got as,

$$\mathbf{v} = \frac{\mathbf{V}}{\mathbf{A_w}} = \frac{12000}{4.5} = 2666.7 \text{ psi}$$

Since the allowable shear stress for A36 steel from Table 4.1.1 is 14500 psi, the section is very safe in shear.

Finally the deflection of the beam will be checked. A simply supported beam with a uniformly distributed load has a maximum deflection, obtained from Fig. 84 as,

$$\delta = \frac{5}{384} \frac{\mathbf{WL^3}}{\mathbf{EI}} \text{--} 33$$

where,

$$\mathbf{W} = \text{total load} = 800 \times 30 = 24000 \text{ lbs}$$
$$\mathbf{L} = \text{the span} = 30 \times 12 = 360 \text{ in.}$$
$$\mathbf{E} = 30 \times 10^6 \text{ psi and,}$$
$$\mathbf{I} = 446.3 \text{ in.}^4$$

The quantities are now dimensionally compatible and may be substituted into Eqn. 33 to obtain a value of deflection $\delta = 1.09$ in.

Assuming that the ceiling cannot suffer damage, a deflection of $\frac{1}{240}$ span will be considered as acceptable, as given in Table 5.9.1. The permissible deflection is hence,

$$\delta_{\text{permissible}} = \frac{1}{240} \times 360 = 1.50 \text{ in.}$$

The actual deflection that the beam will have is less than the maximum that is permitted by the Codes and so the section is acceptable.

Use a W16 $\times$ 36 lbs/ft section for the beam. It should be pointed out here that this section is far from being the only one that can be used. Several sections which satisfy the criteria considered are available and could safely be used. In that case, the Architect has to choose one of several alternative sections for his design. Since the cost of the steelwork is based on the weight of steelwork, the lightest section is usually the cheapest and most economical one. The lightest section may however be deep and if headroom considerations are not critical should certainly be chosen. Otherwise a shallower but a little heavier section may be used.

Example 5.9.2

Design the timber purlin of the carport of Example 2.9.2 and shown in Fig. 16.

In Example 2.9.2 it was determined that the total load on an internal purlin was 1004 lbs. The span of the purlin **L** is 16 ft. The maximum bending moment at the center of the purlin is,

$$\mathbf{BM} = \frac{\mathbf{WL}}{8} = \frac{1004 \times 16}{8} = 2008 \text{ lb ft}$$

$$\mathbf{BM} = 2008 \times 12 = 24096 \text{ lb in.}$$

Use a bending stress of 1200 psi. The compression or upper face of the beam receives adequate lateral support from the plastics sheeting and so no reduction in this value is necessary. Normal duration of loading and dry conditions may also be assumed. A depth factor $\mathbf{C_d}$ has to be allowed for and this is given by,

$$\mathbf{C_d} = 0.81 \left(\frac{\mathbf{d^2 + 143}}{\mathbf{d^2 + 88}} \right) \quad \text{---} \quad 34$$

The depth factor applies only if the depth is greater than 12 in., but not otherwise. Using Eqn. 24,

$$\mathbf{S} = \frac{\mathbf{M}}{\mathbf{f_b}} = \frac{24096}{1200} = 20 \text{ in.}^3$$

Try a 2 in. $\times$ 10 in. nominal section. After planing, the finished section actually is $1\frac{5}{8}$ in. $\times$ $9\frac{1}{2}$ in. The section modulus **S** for the section is,

$$\mathbf{S} = \frac{\mathbf{bd^2}}{6} = \frac{1.625 \times 9.5^2}{6} = 24.4 \text{ in.}^3$$

The section is hence acceptable. Since the depth is less than 12 in. there is no depth effect and $\mathbf{C_d} = 1$.

Check for shear

Using Eqn. 28,

$$\mathbf{f_s} = 1.5 \frac{\mathbf{V}}{\mathbf{bd}} = 1.5 \times \frac{502}{1.625 \times 9.5} = 48.8 \text{ psi}$$

This is well below the maximum permissible shear stress of 95 psi for sawn lumber given in Table 4.3.1, and so the section is safe.

Check for deflection

The maximum deflection at the center, from Eqn. 33 can be got as,

$$\delta = \frac{5}{384} \frac{\mathbf{WL^3}}{\mathbf{EI}} = \frac{5}{384} \frac{1004 \times (16 \times 12)^3 \times 12}{1.76 \times 10^6 \times 1.625 \times 9.5^3} = 0.453 \text{ in.}$$

In the above calculation, the total load $\mathbf{W} = \mathbf{wL}$, $\mathbf{I} = \dfrac{\mathbf{bd}^3}{12}$, and $\mathbf{E} = 1.76 \times 10^6$ psi.

The permissible deflection for a roof purlin, according to Table 5.9.1, is $\dfrac{1}{180}$ span.

$$\delta_{\text{permissible}} = \frac{1}{180} \times 16 \times 12 = 1.07 \text{ in.}$$

The actual deflection is less than the permissible deflection and the section chosen is hence acceptable.

The design of steel and timber beams have now been briefly considered. The design of beams in reinforced concrete is a little more complex because the concrete and the steel reinforcement behave as one composite material. The design of reinforced concrete beams is hence considered separately.

5.10 Ultimate load design of reinforced concrete beams

To design in reinforced concrete it is necessary to understand the behavior of the material and unfortunately this behavior is not the same at working loads, under which the structure operates, as it is at ultimate loads when failure is about to occur. The design for working loads is based on permissible stresses in concrete and steel being reached when the working loads act on the structure.

Consider a simple singly reinforced concrete beam in bending as shown in Fig. 85a. Under **working loads,** the strain diagram is linear, the strain at the neutral axis being zero. The stress diagram for concrete in compression is also linear, the maximum value of the compressive stress $\mathbf{fc}$ being reached at the extreme fiber, as shown in Fig. 85a. Concrete however, cannot take any tension and so all the tension is taken by the steel reinforcement. The compressive forces in the concrete have a resultant $\mathbf{C}$ which acts at the centroid of the triangular stress block whilst the total tensile force $\mathbf{T}$ acts at the center of the steel reinforcement. Between them they form a couple which has an internal resisting moment whose value is equal to the external applied moment that the beam is required to take—and which has already been determined from the bending moment diagram. This enables the stresses in the steel and concrete to be calculated and checked. The design is called a **balanced design** when the permissible stress in concrete (for the concrete chosen) is reached at the same time as the permissible stress in the steel and the internal moment that the beam is capable of developing at that time is equal to the externally applied moment on it. When this occurs it can be shown that **approximately** the moment $\mathbf{M}$ applied to the beam is,

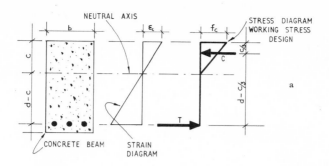

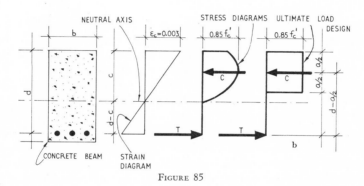

FIGURE 85

$$M = \frac{1}{6} fc \times bd^2 \dotfill 35$$

where,

fc = the permissible stress in concrete as given in Table 4.2.1.

b = width of the section,

d = **effective depth** of the section. This is defined as the depth from the compression face to the center of the steel reinforcement as shown in Fig. 85a.

The amount of steel reinforcement A_s that is necessary for balanced design depends on the strength of the concrete chosen and can be expressed as a percentage of the concrete area **bd** as shown in Table 5.10.1. This is working stress design.

In ultimate load design the approach is quite different. As we have seen in 1.6.2, the working loads are increased by the factor of safety, that is relevant to the type of load on the beam, and the beam is then designed so that failure would just occur under this hypothetical ultimate load. The designer is not concerned with the behavior of the beam at working loads. In order to be able to design at ultimate loads, it is necessary to know the

Table 5.10.1

PERCENTAGE REINFORCEMENT FOR WORKING STRESS DESIGN

Specified compressive strength of concrete fc' psi	Reinforcement as a percentage of the concrete area bd_{eff} for working stress balanced design
3000	1.25
4000	1.40
5000	1.60
6000	1.85

behavior of reinforced concrete as a material at ultimate loads. It has been found that whilst the strain diagram is still linear, as shown in Fig. 85b, the stress in concrete is no longer linear, but is as shown by the parabolic stress distribution of Fig. 85b. The maximum stress in concrete at failure has been found to be 0.85 fc' where fc' is the strength of the concrete chosen. The steel is still assumed to take all the tension and the total internal compressive and tensile forces **C** and **T** form, as before, a couple whose value is equal to the externally applied ultimate moment on the beam.

A parabolic stress distribution in the concrete is rather difficult to work with in the calculations and so the Code ACI 318-71 suggests that the stress distribution in concrete could be assumed to be a simple rectangular stress block as has been shown in Fig. 85b. This does help to simplify the calculations, but in order to keep the total internal force **C** the same as in the previous case, the stress distribution is considered to extend only to a distance **a** and not all the way to the neutral axis which is at a distance **c** from the

Table 5.10.2

RATIO $\dfrac{a}{c}$

Specified compressive strength of concrete fc' psi	$\dfrac{a}{c}$
2500	0.85
3000	0.85
3500	0.85
4000	0.85
5000	0.80
6000	0.75

compression face. The ratio $\dfrac{a}{c}$ is itself a function of the concrete chosen and has been shown, for different strengths of concrete, in Table 5.10.2.

It now only needs the value of **c**, the depth of the neutral axis, to be able to design. For this we make reference again to **balanced design,** which in ultimate load design of reinforced concrete beams is defined as one where the strain in concrete reaches 0.003 when the steel reaches its specified yield stress f_y. The value of **c** will hence depend on the type of steel used but with $f_y = 60000$ psi and $E = 29 \times 10^6$ psi, gives a value of $c = 0.59d$.

Consider once again the beam shown in Fig. 85b, where **b** is the width of the beam and **d** is the effective depth. The total internal force **C** can be determined as,

$$C = \text{stress} \times \text{area over which that stress acts}$$

$$C = 0.85 \ fc' \times ab \ \text{..} \ 36$$

The total internal force **T** can be got as,

$$T = f_y \ A_s \ \text{..} \ 37$$

The lever arm between the two forces is $\left(d - \dfrac{a}{2} \right)$ and so the internal moment M_u that the beam develops at failure is,

$$M_u = \phi \ 0.85 \ fc' \times ab \times \left(d - \dfrac{a}{2} \right) = \phi \ f_y \ A_s \times \left(d - \dfrac{a}{2} \right) \ \text{................} \ 38$$

where,

$$\phi = \text{a capacity reduction factor.}$$

This capacity reduction factor needs a little explanation. It is provided by the Code to increase safety and applies not only to beams in bending but

Table 5.10.3
CAPACITY REDUCTION FACTOR

Method of load transfer	ϕ
Bending	0.90
Shear and torsion	0.85
Compression	
spirally reinforced columns	0.75
tied columns	0.70
Axial tension	0.90

to shear, torsion and columns as well. The capacity reduction factors for different cases are given in Table 5.10.3.

The only other condition laid down by the Code is that the area of reinforcement A_s should not be greater than 75% of that given for balanced design. The reason for this stipulation is to force the beam to fail in tension, if failure ever occurs, by the yielding of the reinforcement rather than by the crushing of the concrete, which latter failure would be catastrophic.

For a given section, all the values in Eqn. 38 have now been determined and it is easy to calculate the ultimate carrying capacity M_u of the beam or alternately to design the beam for a given M_u. The Engineer uses a more complex procedure but for Architects the above approach is entirely appropriate and leads to equally valid results.

The beam has then to be checked for shear. The Code suggests that the shear stress be checked at a distance d, the effective depth, away from the face of the support. Design can be carried out more easily however, by checking the shear stress for the maximum shear force at the face of the support. The shear stress is given by,

$$v_u = \frac{V_u}{\phi\, bd} \quad\quad\quad\quad\quad 39$$

where ϕ is the capacity reduction factor as given in Table 5.10.3.

The value of v_u should be less than v_c the ultimate shear strength for concrete where,

$$v_c = 2\sqrt{fc'} \quad\quad\quad\quad\quad 40$$

If the actual ultimate shear stress v_u is greater than v_c shear reinforcement has to be provided in the beam. This can take the form of either bent up bars or vertical stirrup steel as shown in Fig. 55. The Architect is not really concerned with the design of shear reinforcement. The values of v_c for different concrete strengths fc' are given in Table 5.10.4.

Table 5.10.4
SHEAR STRENGTH v_c OF CONCRETE psi

Specified compressive strength of concrete fc' psi	v_c
3000	110
4000	126
5000	141

Finally the beam has to be checked for deflection unless the depth of the beam is greater than the values given in Table 5.10.5. This Table is important since it gives the Architect the minimum depth that his beam must have for a deflection check to be unnecessary. Though the depth of the beam depends on several factors such as the loading on the beam, the span, the width chosen, etc, the depths as given in Table 5.10.5 are a good preliminary indication of the approximate depth.

Table 5.10.5
MINIMUM OVERALL DEPTHS OF BEAMS OR ONE WAY SLABS

Member	Simply supported	One end continuous	Both ends continuous	Cantilever
Solid one way slabs	$\dfrac{L}{20}$	$\dfrac{L}{24}$	$\dfrac{L}{28}$	$\dfrac{L}{10}$
Beams	$\dfrac{L}{16}$	$\dfrac{L}{18.5}$	$\dfrac{L}{21}$	$\dfrac{L}{8}$

It should finally be noted here that whilst working stress design is simpler and is more useful for the design of complex concrete structures such as folded plates or shells, it is now required that reinforced concrete beams and one way slabs be designed by Ultimate load design.

Example 5.10.1

Design the simply supported main beam of the corridor of the office building of Example 2.9.1 and shown in Fig. 12. The corridor may be assumed to be enclosed by a low concrete parapet wall, 3 ft high and 4 in. thick. Use ultimate load design. Assume **fc′** $= 3000$ psi, **f$_y$** $= 60000$ psi and **b** $= 12$ in.

The superimposed load on the main beam from the floor slab was determined as 720 lbs/ft. Assume that the dead load of the beam is 280 lbs/ft. The weight of the low parapet wall can be determined as,

$$\mathbf{w}_{parapet} = \frac{4}{12} \times 3 \times 1 \times 144 = 144 \text{ lbs/ft} = 150 \text{ lbs/ft say.}$$

We have to first determine the total ultimate load for purposes of design.

The live load component of the load on the beam $= 100 \times 4 = 400$ lbs/ft.

The dead load component of the load on the beam $= 80 \times 4 + 280 + 150 = 750$ lbs/ft.

The Ultimate load **U** on the beam can be determined from a modified Eqn. 2 as,

$$\mathbf{U} = 1.4 \, \mathbf{D.L} + 1.7 \, \mathbf{L.L} \quad \text{..} \quad 41$$

$$\mathbf{U} = 1.4 \times 750 + 1.7 \times 400 = 1730 \text{ lbs/ft.}$$

$$\mathbf{BM}_{max} = \frac{\mathbf{WL}}{8} = \frac{1730 \times 30^2}{8} = 194625 \text{ lb ft.}$$

Since the area of steel that will be provided is only 75% of that required for balanced design, the ultimate balanced design moment $\mathbf{M}_{ub}$ as an approximation can be determined as,

$$\mathbf{M}_{ub} = \frac{194625}{0.75} = 259500 \text{ lb ft.}$$

The maximum ultimate shear force is,

$$\mathbf{V}_u = \frac{1730 \times 30}{2} = 25950 \text{ lbs.}$$

Now $\mathbf{b} = 12$ in., $\mathbf{c} = 0.59\mathbf{d}$ and from Table 5.10.2, $\mathbf{a} = 0.85\mathbf{c}$. From Table 5.10.3 $\phi = 0.90$. Using Eqn. 38, we have,

$$\mathbf{M}_{ub} = \phi\, 0.85 \mathbf{fc}' \times \mathbf{ab} \times \left(\mathbf{d} - \frac{\mathbf{a}}{2} \right)$$

$$259500 \times 12 = 0.90 \times 0.85 \times 3000 \times (0.85 \times 0.59\mathbf{d}) \times 12 \times \left(\mathbf{d} - \frac{0.50\mathbf{d}}{2} \right)$$

This gives,

$$\mathbf{d}^2 = 300.6$$

$$\mathbf{d} = \sqrt{300.6} = 17.34 \text{ in.}$$

The area of steel reinforcement required $\mathbf{A}_s$ can also be determined from Eqn. 38 as,

$$\mathbf{M}_{ub} = \phi\, \mathbf{f}_y\, \mathbf{A}_s \left(\mathbf{d} - \frac{\mathbf{a}}{2} \right)$$

$$259500 \times 12 = 0.90 \times 60000 \times \mathbf{A}_s \times \left(17.34 - \frac{0.50 \times 17.34}{2} \right)$$

Therefore,

$$\mathbf{A}_s = 4.43 \text{ sq in.}$$

The actual steel has to be only 75% of that for balanced design and so the actual area of steel to be provided is $0.75 \times 4.43 = 3.32$ sq in.

Use #10 bar, diameter $= 1.27$ in., area $= 1.27$ sq in.

$$\text{Number of bars required} = \frac{3.32}{1.27} = 2.61 \text{ say 3 nos.}$$

All calculations have been related to **d**, the effective depth to the center of the steel reinforcement. A certain amount of cover of concrete has to be provided to the steel reinforcement firstly to develop proper bond between the concrete and the steel and secondly to prevent the steel from rusting. The clear cover that has to be provided to the steel, for different applications, is given in Table 5.10.6. The overall depth of the beam can hence be obtained as,

$$d_{overall} = d_{effective} + \text{half diameter of bar} + \text{clear cover} \quad \text{............................} \quad 42$$

Table 5.10.6
MINIMUM CLEAR COVER TO REINFORCEMENT in.

Slabs and walls not exposed to the weather	¾ in.
Slabs and walls exposed to the weather	1½ in.
Beams and columns not exposed to the weather	1½ in.
Beams and columns exposed to the weather	2 in.
All members cast against and permanently exposed to earth	3 in.
Thin folded plates or shells	½ in.

Since our beam may very likely be exposed to the weather, the clear cover according to Table 5.10.6 is 2 in. The overall depth of the beam is therefore,

$$d_{overall} = 17.34 + 0.64 + 2.00 = 19.98 \text{ in. say } 20 \text{ in.}$$

Check for shear

$V_u = 25950$ lbs. Using Eqn 39 we have,

$$v_u = \frac{V_u}{\phi \, bd} = \frac{25950}{0.85 \times 12 \times 17.4} = 146 \text{ psi.}$$

The ultimate shear strength v_c is 110 psi for $fc' = 3000$ psi according to Table 5.10.4. Shear reinforcement is hence necessary for the beam.

Check for deflection

According to Table 5.10.5, the minimum overall depth necessary for the beam, so that deflection need not be checked, is $\frac{L}{16}$.

$$\text{Overall depth required} = \frac{L}{16} = \frac{30 \times 12}{16} = 22.5 \text{ in.}$$

The overall depth of the beam has therefore to be increased to more than 22.5 in. or a deflection check becomes necessary. Since the parapet wall may introduce some torsion on the beam, due to horizontal loads on the parapet, it is advisable to increase the depth of the beam to say 24 in.

Provide a beam 12 in. × 24 in. The cross section of the beam has been shown in Fig. 86.

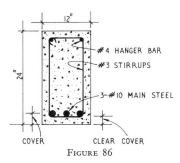

FIGURE 86

5.11 Design of columns subject to axial load

The design of columns in steel and timber when subject only to axial load is based on simple empirical formulae which relate the compressive stress that may be permitted on the cross sectional area of the column to the slenderness ratio of the column. For A36 steel, the AISC gives the permissible stress on main and secondary members for varying slenderness ratios and the values plotted on curves have been shown in Fig. 87. Unlike the values given by the Euler buckling formulae in 5.3, the values as obtained from Fig. 87 are practical realistic values which take into account the fact that columns are never perfectly straight and that small eccentricities of loading will surely occur. The values also have the factor of safety taken into account and so they may be used directly

Example 5.11.1

Determine the maximum actual load that the A36 steel pipe column of Example 5.3.1 can take.

The column has a length of 15 ft and is assumed as pinned at both ends, to that **K** = 1. The radius of gyration **r** = 2.250 in. as determined in Example 5.3.1. The slenderness ratio can hence be got as,

$$\frac{KL}{r} = \frac{1 \times 15 \times 12}{2.250} = 80$$

It may be noted that the slenderness ratio has no units. Referring to Fig. 87 it may be seen that at a slenderness ratio of 80, the permissible stress is 15.4 ksi, on the gross area of the column. The maximum load that the column can safely take is therefore,

$$\mathbf{P} = \mathbf{F_a A} = 15.4 \times 5.581 = 86 \text{ Kips.}$$

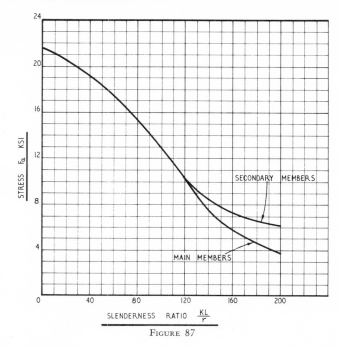

FIGURE 87

This value of 86 K may be compared to the theoretical buckling load of 257 K for the perfect column as obtained in Example 5.3.1, giving some indication of the actual factor of safety involved.

Example 5.11.2

Determine the approximate size of an A36 internal steel column at the base level of a 15 storey high rise building. The columns are spaced at 20 ft on centers and the storey height is 12 ft. The total loading on each floor (dead + live) may be taken as 200 lbs/sq ft and the total loading on the roof (dead + snow) may be assumed as 100 lbs/sq ft.

The total load on the column at the base level of the building taking contributory areas can be determined as,

Load from the roof $= 100 \times 20 \times 20 = 40000$ lbs
Load from the floors $= 200 \times 20 \times 20 \times 14 = 1120,000$ lbs

Total load $= 40000 + 1120,000 = 1160,000$ lbs $= 1160$ K

The weight of the column itself is very small compared to this load and may safely be neglected.

As the column is an internal column, it will have beams framing into it from all four sides. These beams will hold the top end in place. The bottom of the column will be anchored into a foundation and will hence also be held in place. The end conditions are likely to be at least pinned at both ends. The effective length is the same as the actual length and in the calculation for the slenderness ratio $\mathbf{K} = 1$.

Try a W14 $\times$ 202 lbs/ft. The properties of this section as given by the AISC Manual of Steel Construction are,

> Depth of section = 14 in.
> Width of flange = 16 in.
> Area of cross section $\mathbf{A} = 59.39$ sq in.
> The minimum radius of gyration $\mathbf{r}_y = 4.06$ in.

The maximum slenderness ratio (about the **YY** axis) can hence be determined as,

$$\frac{\mathbf{KL}}{\mathbf{r}_y} = \frac{1 \times 12 \times 12}{4.06} = 35.5$$

At this slenderness ratio and referring to Fig. 87, it can be seen that the permissible compressive stress on the gross area of the column is 19.6 ksi. The maximum axial load that the column can take is therefore,

$$\mathbf{P} = \mathbf{F}_a \, \mathbf{A} = 19.6 \times 59.39 = 1164 \text{ K}$$

The actual load on the column is 1160 K and so the column section is safe and hence acceptable.

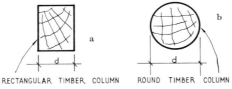

RECTANGULAR TIMBER COLUMN   ROUND TIMBER COLUMN

FIGURE 88

The design of timber columns is also based on empirical formulae as given by the AITC. Solid timber columns can be either rectangular as shown in Fig. 88a or round as shown in Fig. 88b.

For rectangular timber columns, the allowable stress in compression $\mathbf{F}_a$ on the gross area of the column and parallel to the grain is given by,

$$\mathbf{F}_a = \frac{0.30 \times \mathbf{E}}{\left(\dfrac{\mathbf{L}}{\mathbf{d}} \right)^2} \hspace{4cm} 43$$

where,

> $\mathbf{L} = $ unsupported length of the column,

$$d = \text{least dimension of the column,}$$

$$E = \text{modulus of elasticity of timber.}$$

For round columns,

$$F_a = \frac{0.226 \times E}{\left(\dfrac{L}{d}\right)^2} \cdots\cdots\cdots\cdots\cdots\cdots\cdots\cdots\cdots\cdots\cdots\cdots\cdots\cdots\cdots\cdots\cdots\cdots\cdots\cdots\cdots\cdots\cdots\cdots \quad 44$$

It can be seen that for timber columns, the allowable compressive stress has been related to the $\dfrac{L}{d}$ ratio which is also a measure of its slenderness. It should also be noted that the value of F_a as obtained from Eqns. 43 and 44 cannot exceed under any circumstances the allowable maximum compressive stress parallel to the grain for the material specified, as given in Table 4.3.1 and adjusted for duration of loading, wet and dry conditions, etc, since this latter value is the allowable stress for the crushing of the material as a short column.

Example 5.11.3

Design a square timber column to carry a load of 40000 lbs. The height of the column is 10 ft. The maximum allowable compressive stress is 1200 psi. $E = 1.76 \times 10^6$ psi.

Try a column size 6 in. $\times$ 6 in. The gross area of the column is then,

$$A = 6 \times 6 = 36 \text{ sq in.}$$

$$\frac{L}{d} = \frac{10 \times 12}{6} = 20$$

From Eqn. 43 we have,

$$F_a = \frac{0.30 \times E}{\left(\dfrac{L}{d}\right)^2} = \frac{0.30 \times 1.76 \times 10^6}{400} = 1320 \text{ psi.}$$

Since this value of F_a is greater than 1200 psi, the maximum that can be allowed on the column is 1200 psi. The load P that the column can take is therefore,

$$P = F_a \, A = 1200 \times 36 = 43200 \text{ lbs.}$$

Since the load P that the column can take is greater than 40000 lbs, the column is safe and the section is hence acceptable.

Example 5.11.4

Design a round timber post to carry a load of 40000 lbs on a height of 15 ft. The maximum allowable compressive stress is 1200 psi. $E = 1.76 \times 10^6$ psi.

Try a timber post 8 in. in diameter.

$$A = \frac{\pi d^2}{4} = \frac{\pi 8^2}{4} = 50.27 \text{ sq in.} \qquad \frac{L}{d} = \frac{15 \times 12}{8} = 22.5$$

Using Eqn. 44 we have,

$$F_a = \frac{0.226 \times 1.76 \times 10^6}{506.25} = 786 \text{ psi}$$

The value of F_a is less than 1200 psi and so is the more critical for the column. The load that the column can take is therefore,

$$P = F_a A = 786 \times 50.27 = 39512 \text{ lbs.}$$

This value of the load is close enough to the load of 40000 lbs that the post is required to take and so the section is acceptable.

5.12 Ultimate load design of reinforced concrete columns

As we have seen in 4.2, reinforced concrete columns can be of two types. If the main longitudinal steel is held by rectangular ties, as in Fig. 56a, the column is called a **tied column**. If the main longitudinal steel however, is arranged in a circle and held by spiral reinforcement, as shown in Fig. 56b, it is called a **spirally reinforced column**. It may be noted that the terms are not strictly related to the shape of the column since a spirally reinforced column can be square in section. For purposes of calculation however, only the equivalent circular column is considered.

The design of only short, axially loaded reinforced concrete columns is being considered here. Nevertheless, even for such a column, the Code ACI 318-71 specifies that the column must be designed for a small eccentricity of load **e** which depends on the size and type of column but cannot be less than 1 in. For a preliminary analysis and design by the Architect however, this eccentricity can be neglected and the column designed with great ease and simplicity by the formula,

$$P_u = \phi \left[0.85 fc' \times (A_g - A_s) + A_s f_y \right] \quad \text{.......................... 45}$$

where,

P_u = ultimate load on the column
ϕ = capacity reduction factor as given in Table 5.10.3
fc' = ultimate crushing strength of concrete
A_g = gross area of the column
A_s = area of steel provided
f_y = yield stress of the steel used.

The first term in the above Eqn. 45 gives the ultimate load that the net concrete area can take and the second term gives the load that the steel can take. The two terms together hence give the total ultimate load that the column can take.

The main longitudinal steel reinforcement for any reinforced concrete column cannot be less than 1% nor more than 8%.

Example 5.12.1

Design the column of Example 5.11.2 as a short tied reinforced concrete column. $fc' = 4000$ psi, $f_y = 60000$ psi. The live load and dead load components of the load may be assumed to be equal.

The live load and dead load components of the working load are each equal to 580 K. The ultimate load P_u that the column has to take can hence be determined as,

$$P_u = 1.4\ \textbf{D.L.} + 1.7\ \textbf{L.L.}$$
$$P_u = 1.4 \times 580 + 1.7 \times 580 = 812 + 986 = 1798\ K.$$

Try a square column 24 in. × 24 in. Then using Eqn. 45 we have,

$$1798,000 = 0.70\ [0.85 \times 4000 \times (24 \times 24 - A_s) + A_s \times 60000]$$

The value of A_s can hence be calculated as 10.78 sq in. This area for A_s lies between 1% (5.76 sq in.) and 8% (46.08 sq in.) and the column is hence acceptable.

Use #9 bars, bar diameter = 1.128 in., cross sectional area of each bar = 1.00 sq in.

$$\text{Number of bars required} = \frac{10.78}{1.00} = 10.78\ \text{say 12 nos.}$$

The cross section of the column is shown in Fig. 89.

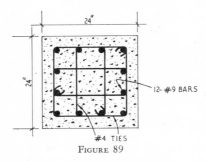

FIGURE 89

5.13 Ultimate load design of reinforced concrete walls

Reinforced concrete walls are often used in building construction and the ultimate load design of such walls will be briefly considered here. If the wall has lateral loading on it, this has to be taken into account and the wall designed as a retaining wall. If the walls are simple load bearing, axially loaded concrete walls, then the ultimate load on the wall should be less than P_u where,

$$P_u = 0.55 \, \phi \, fc' \, A_g \left[1 - \left(\frac{L}{40h} \right)^2 \right] \quad\text{---} \quad 46$$

where,

> $\phi =$ capacity reduction factor $= 0.70$
> $fc' =$ specified ultimate compressive strength of concrete
> $A_g =$ gross area of the wall per foot of wall
> $L =$ vertical height of the wall between supports
> $h =$ overall thickness of the wall.

The Code ACI 318-71 specifies certain minimum thicknesses of such walls. The load bearing concrete wall of a building cannot be less than 6 in. thick. If it is merely a panel or enclosure wall, it cannot be less than 4 in. thick. Exterior basement or foundation walls cannot be less than 8 in. thick. A cross section through two load bearing concrete walls is shown in Fig. 90. The

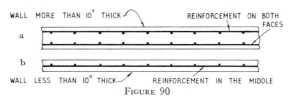

WALL MORE THAN 10" THICK   REINFORCEMENT ON BOTH FACES

a

b

WALL LESS THAN 10" THICK   REINFORCEMENT IN THE MIDDLE

FIGURE 90

design of a simple axially loaded reinforced concrete wall will now be considered.

Example 5.13.1

Design a load bearing reinforced concrete wall to carry a dead load of 22000 lbs/ft and a live load of 22000 lbs/ft. The height of the wall is 12 ft. $fc' = 4000$ psi.

Assume that the wall is 6 in. thick and consider a 1 ft strip of the wall. The ultimate load P_u that this 1 ft length has to take is,

$$P_u = 1.4 \times 22000 + 1.7 \times 22000 = 68200 \text{ lbs/ft.}$$

Using Eqn. 46 we have the load that the 6 in. thick wall can actually take as,

$$P_u = 0.55 \times 0.70 \times 4000 \times 12 \times 6 \left[1 - \left(\frac{12 \times 12}{40 \times 6} \right)^2 \right] = 70963 \text{ lbs/ft}$$

$P_u = 71000$ lbs/ft say.

Since the wall has to take only 68200 lbs/ft and can actually take 71000 lbs/ft it is safe. The cross section of the wall would be of the type shown in Fig. 90b with spot welded wire mesh reinforcement placed in the middle of the wall.

5.14 Connections

It would be quite inappropriate to show all the types of connections in steel, concrete and timber in a book on Structures for Architects. Connections between members should really be covered in the Building Technology course that Architectural students are required to take. But connections are important to design and lack of proper attention to the detailing of connections can easily convert a good design into a bad one.

Some typical timber connections have already been shown in 4.3. Poured in place reinforced concrete presents no problems since the joint becomes monolithic. Precast prestressed concrete however, needs specialised joints and these may be found in the **PCI Design Handbook** issued by the Prestressed Concrete Institute. Complete information on connections for steel will be found in the AISC Manual of Steel Construction. It is important to detail the connection so that the assumptions made in the design are realised. Consider for instance, a haunched built up steel girder which is to have rigid connections with the columns as shown in Fig. 91. For ease of erection, a bolted cleat connection is provided on the web of the girder but after the girder has been erected in place, the flanges are welded to the small seating strips on the columns (which are welded to the girder) to yield a rigid connection.

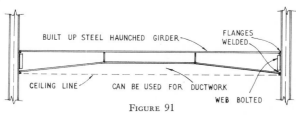

BUILT UP STEEL HAUNCHED GIRDER FLANGES WELDED

CEILING LINE   CAN BE USED FOR DUCTWORK   WEB BOLTED

FIGURE 91

Two other inportant factors need consideration. The first is that various materials have to act together and can and do help each other. An example of this is the simple connection of the secondary beam loading on to a main beam, as shown in Fig. 92. The reinforced concrete slab loads on to the secondary beam and affords adequate lateral support to the compression flange at the same time as well. The flange of the secondary beam is cut to enable the web to be bolted through cleat angles to the web of the main beam. The connection of the main beam to the column is shown in Fig. 93. The seating angle is welded to the column and helps erection. The main beam is

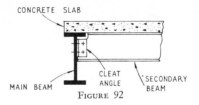

FIGURE 92

bolted to the web of the column with the help of cleat angles as shown in Fig. 93.

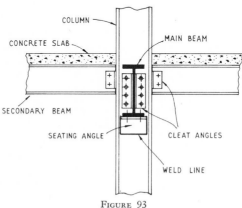

FIGURE 93

The second important factor that needs to be kept in mind in detailing the connections is the integration of the mechanical system with the structural system. In order to distribute large volumes of air to distant parts of the building requires an efficient ducting system. If improperly detailed, the structural system can interfere with the flow of air, or at least require a more expensive ceiling than would otherwise be necessary. The provision of ducts with precast prestressed concrete members has been discussd in 4.2 and two typical examples have been shown in Figs. 57 and 58. Another typical example of the way in which ducts and trenches for services can be provided is shown, for a main steel beam with composite steel deck and concrete topping, in Fig. 94. The concrete provides fire protection but beneath the duct and

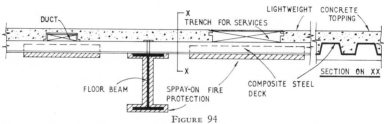

FIGURE 94

the trench as also on the steel beam itself a spray-on fire protection can be used.

Problems for solution

Example 1: A structural glued laminated timber cantilever overhang is shown in Fig. 95. The cantilevers have a span L = 6.5 ft and are spaced at 12 ft on centers. If the snow load is 40 lbs/sq ft and a load at the tip of 200 lbs concentrated (a maintenance man) has to be allowed for, design the maximum section of the cantilever at the face of the column. Actual allowable f_b = 2000 psi. f_s = 165 psi.

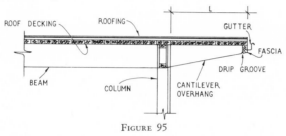

FIGURE 95

Ans: Total distributed load = 57 lbs/sq ft, Beam size 3⅛ in. × 13½ in. Neglect the dead load of the beam itself.

Example 2: Design the one way reinforced concrete floor slab of the corridor of the office building of Example 2.9.1 and shown in Fig. 12. Use working stress design. fc' = 3000 psi.

Ans: Fig. 96.

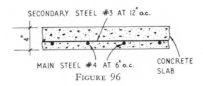

FIGURE 96

Example 3: Design the main glued laminated timber beam of Example 2.9.2 and shown in Fig. 16. f_b actual = 2000 psi. f_s = 165 psi.

Ans: 3⅛ in. × 15 in.

Example 4: Design a short tied reinforced concrete column to take a dead load of 100000 lbs and a live load of 100000 lbs. Use ultimate load design. fc' = 4000 psi. f_y = 60000 psi.

Ans: Fig. 97.

Example 5: After a careful study of this Chapter, design approximately

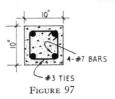

FIGURE 97

the structural components of the structural system in your Architectural design. The components may be designed for tension, compression, bending moment, shear force and deflections only, in steel, concrete or timber.

Hint: First verbalise the structural behavior of the system as in Example 6 in Problems for solution at the end of Chapter 3. Estimate the loads and then commence the design for the components from the roof coming downwards. Make any assumptions and approximations you feel necessary to reduce your case to standard cases. Consult your structures critic as needed.

Example 6: For the design in Example 5 above, show a few typical connection details between the members of your structure.

Chapter 6

DESIGN OF ELEMENTARY STRUCTURAL SYSTEMS USING HANDBOOKS

6.1 Design with handbooks

The general principles of structural design have now been covered. The load propagation through simple structural systems such as beam and post, arches, trusses, etc, has been appreciated. Design or sizing for the various elements of the structural system in tension, compression, bending and shear can also be carried out.

In the majority of normal or standard cases however, for simple structures of this type, it is quite unnecessary to have to actually work through sizing calculations. The reason is that most of these simple systems are now prefabricated and commercially manufactured. Decking in timber or steel, beams in glued laminated timber or steel, open web joists in steel, hollow core slabs, single or double tees in prestressed concrete, columns in steel or concrete, arches in glued laminated timber, etc, are a few typical examples of the elementary systems that the Architect can use.

Each manufacturer of any of these structural systems would naturally prefer to see the Architect use his product. As part of the service to the Architect therefore, and thereby to encourage the use and sale of his system, the manufacturer provides in his descriptive and technical trade literature or catalog, complete information on the load that the various sizes of members in that system can take over various spans and spacings—all calculated in conformity with the Code regulations for the particular material. The information that he provides, in order to be perfectly general, covers a wide range of loadings, spans, spacings, etc. If the Architect can determine his span, his spacing and his load, he can abstract the size of the member that would be suitable directly from the literature. Naturally the Architect has to be able to understand the technical literature as provided by the various manufacturers, which is not always easy because each manufacturer may choose to present his data in a different way. It is in being able to understand, correctly interpret and use intelligently the information that the manufacturer has provided that the Architect needs to appreciate the "structures" in the first five Chapters of this book. There is also another very valid reason why he should not attempt to use Handbooks without a prior understanding of the structural theory that has led the manufacturer to recommend a particular size for a particular span and a particular loading. The reason is that whilst the manufacturer attempts to be as general as possible, he cannot possibly cover all cases that the Architect is likely to meet with in practice. The Architect therefore needs to have a sufficient knowledge of structures to make correct approximations to reduce his non-standard case down to a reasonably equivalent case that the manufacturer has in his literature.

Finally it should be noted here that such technical design data is not necessarily obtained only from trade literature. Very often it is available in Handbooks that are published by the Associations or Institutes that govern the use of the materials. Handbooks giving vast amounts of excellent design data for quick and easy reference are published by the American Institute of Steel Construction (AISC), the Prestressed Concrete Institute (PCI), the American Concrete Institute (ACI), the Portland Cement Association (PCA), the American Institute of Timber Construction (AITC) and the Aluminum Association.

As may be very easily appreciated, it is impossible to take the design, using Handbooks or trade literature, of every system currently available. New and improved systems appear on the market every year and so all such designs would soon both be incomplete as well as out of date. The principles governing such design however, leading to a choice of member, do not change and it is these principles that we will attempt to understand through a few simple examples in this Chapter.

6.2 Design examples using handbooks

Let us examine some typical alternative structural arrangements in timber, steel and concrete for the roofing of an area 40 ft × 120 ft. The snow load is 25 lbs/sq ft. A five ply built up tar and gravel roof (non-structural) has to be provided with some thermal insulation. The problem is to design the structural roof using Handbooks and Trade literature.

The Architectural design has produced an area of 40 ft × 120 ft. A large number of possible alternative arrangements are possible in timber, steel and concrete and in a combination of these materials. It is therefore not possible to examine all systems, but to illustrate the principles involved five typical arrangements will be considered here. It is assumed that in all cases, adequate drainage can be provided to the roof by sloping the members or by cambering.

Example 6.2.1 Timber decking on glued laminated beams

It is proposed to use a solid, heavy double tongue and groove timber decking on structural glued laminated beams. These are shown in Fig. 98. The

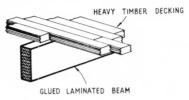

HEAVY TIMBER DECKING

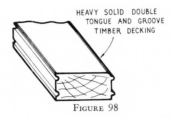

GLUED LAMINATED BEAM

HEAVY SOLID DOUBLE
TONGUE AND GROOVE
TIMBER DECKING

FIGURE 98

beams, whether in timber or steel, span the 40 ft dimension and are supported on main beams which span between columns on the 120 ft side. The design of the main beams and the columns on the 120 ft side do not concern us and will not be considered here. The deck whether in timber, steel or aluminum then spans between the 40 ft long beams which are appropriately spaced and the spacing of the beams is the span of the decking. This is shown in Fig. 99.

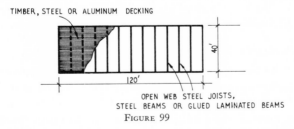

TIMBER, STEEL OR ALUMINUM DECKING

120'

40'

OPEN WEB STEEL JOISTS,
STEEL BEAMS OR GLUED LAMINATED BEAMS
FIGURE 99

The first problem is to determine the spacing of the glued laminated beams. This is dictated by the distance over which the decking chosen can span efficiently and economically for the loading that comes on it. This loading has therefore to be determined. In all design it is necessary to come from the top down.

Loads on the roof

Weight of built up five ply, tar and gravel roof = 6.35 lbs/sq ft

Non-combustible, expanded glass, roof insula-
tion, 1½ in. thick, weight 0.85 lbs/sq ft/in. = 1.27 lbs/sq ft

Snow load .... = 25.0 lbs/sq ft

Total load .... = 32.62 lbs/sq ft

The spacing of the glued laminated beams must be such that the decking can take at least 32.62 lbs/sq ft + its own dead load safely on that span. Try Southern Pine 3 in. × 6 in. solid decking (net 2½ in. × 5¼ in.). From the AITC Handbook **WOOD—A Modern Structural Material**, the Table for solid decking shows that Southern Pine, Commercial grade, 3 in. × 6 in. can take 43 lbs/sq ft on a span of 12 ft with a deflection of $\frac{1}{180}$ span. The dead load of the decking itself is 7.6 lbs/sq ft. Table 5.9.1 shows that for roofs, the deflection will be acceptable. The actual total load on the decking is,

$$\mathbf{w} = 32.62 + 7.60 = 40.22 \text{ lbs/sq ft}$$

Since the decking can take 43 lbs/sq ft it is acceptable. The decking has now been designed. The spacing of the glued laminated beams has also now been determined as 12 ft. Each of these beams spans 40 ft and the load on each of these beams is 40.22 lbs/sq ft superimposed. Referring to the Beam Design Tables for glued laminated beams in the same handbook, it is seen that on a 40 ft span at 12 ft centers, a 5⅛ in. × 24 in. beam can take 40 lbs/sq ft. It would appear at first glance that the beam size was therefore almost acceptable. However careful reading shows that the 40 lbs/sq ft is a **total load** which includes the dead load of the beam itself. One larger size of beam is therefore called for and an acceptable size is hence 5⅛ in. × 25½ in. which can take 45 lbs/sq ft on a 40 ft span and at 12 ft spacing on centers. The adequacy of this beam can be confirmed by determining the actual dead load of the beam and calculating the additional load due to it in lbs/sq ft as follows:

$$\text{Dead load of the beam itself} = \frac{5.125}{12} \times \frac{25.5}{12} \times 40 \times 36 = 1307 \text{ lbs}$$

This assumes that the timber weighs about 36 lbs/cu ft. The load in terms of lbs/sq ft is hence,

$$\mathbf{w} = \frac{1307}{40 \times 12} = 2.72 \text{ lbs/sq ft}$$

The total load on the beam is hence 40.22 + 2.72 = 42.94 lbs/sq ft. Since this is less than the 45 lbs/sq ft load that the beam can safely take, the section is acceptable.

The roof has now been designed, with the help of a Handbook, and a

3 in. × 6 in. heavy, solid Southern Pine decking on 5⅛ in. × 25½ in. glued laminated timber beams spaced 12 ft on centers would be acceptable.

Example 6.2.2 Plywood roof sheathing on secondary rafters supported on glued laminated timber beams

The proposed arrangement is shown in Fig. 100. It consists of plywood roof sheathing panels 4 ft × 8 ft supported on secondary rafters (lumber joists) which are in turn supported on the glued laminated beams spanning 40 ft. The spacing of the glued laminated beams is hence the span of the rafters and the spacing of the rafters is the span of the plywood panels. On the top of the plywood roof sheathing is of course the built up non-structural roof. The load on the plywood panels can once again be calculated exactly as in Example 6.2.1 as 32.62 lbs/sq ft.

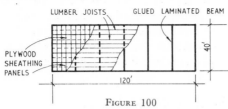

FIGURE 100

Referring to the table for permissible roof loads on plywood panels in the same reference **WOOD—A Modern Structural Material**, it can be seen that a ¾ in. thick 48/24 (panel marking) plywood panel can support safely an allowable live load of 35 lbs/sq ft, on a span of 48 in. with an allowable deflection of $\frac{1}{180}$ span. In the table it is also specifically given that 5 lbs/sq ft has been allowed for the total dead load on the panel giving a total load that the panel can take of 35 + 5 = 40 lbs/sq ft.

Since a ¾ in. plywood panel weighs about 2.25 lbs/sq ft, the total load that the panel is actually required to take is 32.62 + 2.25 = 34.87 lbs/sq ft. The panel is hence acceptable.

The secondary rafters are spaced 4 ft on centers and span 20 ft. The maximum load on an internal rafter is 34.87 lbs/sq ft + Dead load of the rafter itself, say a total of 40 lbs/sq ft.

Referring to the lumber section of the same Handbook shows that tables are available for plain lumber joists or rafters but only for spacings up to 24 in. With a live load (snow) of 30 lbs/sq ft and a dead load of 15 lbs/sq ft, a 2 in. × 12 in. Dense Select Structural type rafter, 24 in. on centers can span 23 ft 3 in. Since the rafters are spaced 48 in. on centers, the loading is double and this is hence equivalent to requiring **two** sections of 2 in. × 12 in.

Provide secondary rafters 2 Nos. 2 in. × 12 in. at 48 in. on centers. The design of the glued laminated beams on which the rafters rest follows the same pattern as discussed in Example 6.2.1 and is not repeated here.

Example 6.2.3 Metal deck on open web steel joists

The general arrangement is shown in Fig. 99 and details are shown in Fig. 101. The built up roof is applied in this case on light weight concrete

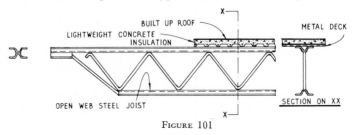

FIGURE 101

insulation which is poured in place on the top of the steel or aluminum metal deck. The deck spans over the open web steel joists which span 40 ft. The spacing of the open web steel joists is the span of the deck. The deck is hence designed first, to determine the economical spacing of the open web steel joists. The total load on the metal deck can be got as,

Five ply built up roof .... = 6.35 lbs/sq ft

Light weight concrete roof insulation, say
2 in. thick over corrugations .... = 10 lbs/sq ft

Snow load .... = 25 lbs/sq ft

Total load .... = 41.35 lbs/sq ft

Use a steel deck of the type shown in Fig. 101 and refer to the Trade literature issued by any one of various steel deck manufacturers. One such type is shown to be capable of taking a total load of 45 lbs/sq ft on a span of 6 ft 6 in., if simple spans are used. The gage thickness of the sheet metal is 22 gage and the weight of the deck is 1.84 lbs/sq ft.

The total load that the steel deck actually has to take is hence 41.35 + 1.84 = 43.19 lbs/sq ft. Since this is less than the allowable value of 45 lbs/sq ft, the deck is acceptable.

The span of the deck is the spacing of the open web steel joists. The joists are hence spaced 6 ft 6 in. on centers and span 40 ft. The total super-imposed load on each internal joist is 43.19 lbs/sq ft over a contributory area of 6.5×40 sq ft.

$$W = 43.19 \times 6.5 \times 40 = 11229 \text{ lbs}$$

A reference is now made to tables for the allowable loads on long span open web steel joists of any particular manufacturer or to the AISC **Manual of Steel Construction.** The tables of one such manufacturer show that a 24 in. deep, open web steel joist of the LH series based on an allowable stress of 30000 psi (high tensile steel) can safely support a total load of 298 lbs/lineal foot. Since the manufacturer's value is in lbs/lineal ft it has to be converted into a total load,

$$\mathbf{W} = 298 \times 40 = 11920 \text{ lbs}$$

The above value of 11920 lbs includes the dead load of the joist itself which has been given in the same table as 12.7 lbs/ft. The actual total load on the joist is therefore,

$$\mathbf{W} = 11229 + 12.7 \times 40 = 11229 + 508 = 11737 \text{ lbs}$$

The actual total load on the joist of 11737 lbs is less than the total load of 11920 lbs which the joist can safely carry and so the section chosen is acceptable.

The manufacturer's Trade literature gives a great deal of information on constructional and bearing details and should be referred to for detailing connections.

Example 6.2.4 Metal deck on steel beams

The general arrangement has been shown in Fig. 99 and details are shown in Fig. 102. The design of the steel deck is exactly the same as in Example 6.2.3. The steel beams are therefore spaced 6 ft 6 in. on centers and span 40 ft. The total load on the steel beam is still 11229 lbs.

For steel beams it is best to refer to the AISC **Manual of Steel Construction.** This manual gives in the beam tables, the total allowable load on a W21 × 44 lbs/ft section as 33 K on a span of 40 ft. The beam is assumed to be laterally supported by the deck which is a realistic assumption. The actual total load on the beam can be got as,

$$\mathbf{W} = 11229 + 44 \times 40 = 11229 + 1760 = 12989 \text{ lbs, say 13 K}$$

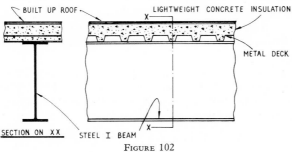

FIGURE 102

It can be seen that the load of 33 K that the steel beam can safely carry is far in excess of the total load of 13 K on it. With the use of the tables however, one cannot use a lighter or shallower section because the manual does not give 40 ft spans for such lighter sections. The reason is that **deflection** becomes very important at such spans and so whilst a lighter I-section could certainly be used, a deflection check would be necessary.

It also becomes clear that for roof loading, which is much lighter than floor loading, an open web steel joist with a weight of 12.7 lbs/ft is lighter and more economical than a steel beam with a weight of 44 lbs/ft.

Example 6.2.5 Precast prestressed concrete double tees

The general arrangement of the roof is shown in Fig. 103a. A built up roof is on top of a concrete topping to the double tees. The concrete topping

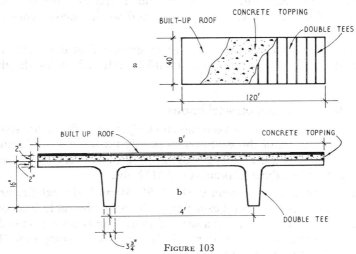

FIGURE 103

serves as insulation as well and so no further insulation is necessary. The total superimposed load on any double tee can be calculated as,

Five ply built up roof .... = 6.35 lbs/sq ft

Snow load .... = 25.0 lbs/sq ft

Total load .... = 31.35 lbs/sq ft

Reference is now made to literature issued by the manufacturers of precast prestressed concrete sections or to the **PCI Design Handbook** issued by the Prestressed Concrete Institute. This handbook shows that an 8DT16 + 2 double tee section of normal weight concrete, as shown in Fig. 103b will carry a safe superimposed live load of 42 lbs/sq ft. The dead load of the double tee itself has already been taken into account by the handbook in calculating this safe load and so should not be considered. This also includes the dead load of the topping. Since the total load of 31.35 lbs/sq ft superimposed on the double tee is less than the value of 42 lbs/sq ft that the double tee can actually take, the section is acceptable. The tables also give considerable other information such as the strength of concrete, the prestressing wire strand pattern, etc which may be of some interest.

6.3 Column design using handbooks

In the examples taken in 6.2 the design of pre-engineered horizontal beam type elements in timber, steel and concrete of various types has been considered. It is possible to design simple columns as well with the use of handbooks and two such examples will be taken here.

Example 6.3.1 Steel columns

Design the A36 steel column of Example 5.11.2.

The column was assumed to be pinned at both ends and the effective length of the column was the same as the actual length of 12 ft. The load on the column was determined as 1160 K.

Referring to the AISC **Manual of Steel Construction,** in the tables on allowable loads on columns, it is found that an A36 W14 × 202 lbs/ft section can take 1161 K on an effective length of 12 ft. The section is hence acceptable.

Example 6.3.2

Design an A36 steel pipe column to take a load of 80 K on an effective length of 15 ft.

Referring to the tables for allowable loads on standard steel pipe in the AISC **Manual of Steel Construction,** it is seen that a 6 in. diameter steel pipe with a wall thickness of 0.280 in. can take a concentric load of 86 K. The section is hence acceptable.

Example 6.3.3 Reinforced concrete columns

Design the column of Example 5.12.1 as a circular spirally reinforced column with the help of a handbook.

The height of the column in Example 5.12.1 was 12 ft and it was assumed to be a short column. The ultimate load on the column was determined as 1798 K. Referring to **Notes on ACI 318-71, Building Code Requirement with Design Applications** published by the Portland Cement Association (PCA), the table on concentrically loaded spirally reinforced round columns is of interest to us. Many choices of column are possible because both the diameter as well as the reinforcement content or percentage can be varied. A 24 in. diameter round column with 6 #11 bars has an ultimate load $P_u = 1801$ K and is acceptable. $fc' = 4000$ psi and $f_y = 60000$ psi. The column is designed for a concentric load but the small eccentricity of load for which the column has to be designed according to ACI 318-71 has been taken into account.

6.4 Conclusions

It should be noted here again that the few examples taken are only a small fraction of the structural elements that can be designed by the use of handbooks or trade literature issued by manufacturers. These sources of information are very valuable and should be readily used. But they should be used with care and with a proper understanding of all the conditions and limitations under which the data is being presented. These conditions are usually put in print with the table or set of tables and should be thoroughly checked to ensure that the particular case being designed is covered by the tables. A little knowledge of structures as obtained from the first five chapters of this book would contribute much towards this objective enabling the Architect to use the information contained in other sources with confidence and care.

Problems for solution

Example 1: In addition to the five systems considered in this Chapter, examine three other alternative systems to roof the area of 40 ft × 120 ft with a flat roof. It may be assumed that proper drainage can be provided to the roof by adequately sloping the members.

Example 2: Using Handbooks or Trade literature, design and detail three alternative methods of providing a structural floor for the stack area of a library 40 ft × 120 ft. Intermediate columns may be provided if necessary.

Chapter 7

SIMPLE STATICALLY INDETERMINATE STRUCTURES

7.1 Introduction

It has been seen in Chapter 3 that statically determinate structural systems are capable of being analysed by the simple rules of statics. The design of the various elements of the structure and the sizing of components can be carried out very easily. Unfortunately not all structural systems are statically determinate. The range of structural systems that fall into the category of being **statically indeterminate** is so vast and so important that a study of statical indeterminacy becomes of some importance to the Architect. Continuous beams, portal frames, grids, plates, folded plates, shells, space frames are all statically indeterminate structures.

The Architect need not of course approach the study of statically indeterminate structures in the same way in which it is approached by the Structural Engineer. The Structural Engineer is after mathematically accurate and exact solutions which satisfy his needs and his training—and even he makes a number of assumptions along the line! The Architect on the other hand is after only reasonably accurate but nevertheless approximate solutions. They are based on simplifying assumptions which provide him with quick answers for an approximate design. The sizes that he determines are hence only approximately correct. They may not be the exact sizes that will be used by the Structural Engineer when the building is finally built. But they are reasonably close for the Architect to determine the general feasibility and relative merits of the structural systems that he is proposing to use, examine headroom considerations and investigate costs.

A simple study of statically indeterminate systems is vital to the good Architect.

7.2 Single span beams

The simple cantilever and the simply supported beam considered in earlier Chapters are examples of statically determinate single span beams. If one or both ends of the simply supported beam are fixed however, the beam becomes statically indeterminate. If only one end is fixed the beam is called a **propped cantilever** since the beam can also be looked upon as a cantilever with a prop at the free end. If both ends of the simply supported beam are fixed, the beam is called a **fixed end** beam.

Consider the propped cantilever shown in Fig. 104a, subjected to a uniformly distributed load **w** lbs/ft. The propped cantilever can be looked upon as a simple cantilever with the uniformly distributed load acting downwards and the unknown reaction of the prop R_B at the free end acting upwards.

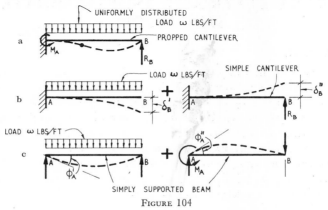

FIGURE 104

This is shown in Fig. 104b. For the beam in Fig. 104b to be a propped cantilever, the tip deflection at the end **B** under both loadings together must be zero. This is an equation of **compatibility** and causes the case of Fig. 104b to return to the actual case of the propped cantilever of Fig. 104a. For the deflection at the end **B,** in Fig. 104b, to be zero it follows that the downward deflection due to the uniformly distributed load must be exactly equal to the upward deflection under the reaction of the prop. The downward deflection under the uniformly distributed load can be obtained from Fig. 84 as,

$$\delta_B' = \frac{wL^4}{8EI}$$

The upward deflection under the prop reaction is again got from Fig. 84,

$$\delta_B'' = \frac{R_BL^3}{3EI}$$

For the beam to be a propped cantilever therefore,

$$\frac{wL^4}{8EI} = \frac{R_BL^3}{3EI}$$

This gives the value of R_B as,

$$R_B = \frac{3wL}{8} = \frac{3W}{8} \text{---} 47$$

where W is the total load on the propped cantilever $= wL$.

The reaction on the prop R_B has now been determined and the bending moment and shear force diagrams for the beam can be drawn by using the principles discussed in Chapter 3, and are shown in Fig. 105.

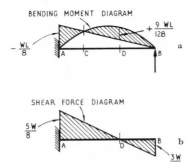

BENDING MOMENT DIAGRAM

SHEAR FORCE DIAGRAM

FIGURE 105

The propped cantilever could also have been analysed by considering it to be a simply supported beam loaded with the uniformly distributed load acting downward and acted upon by an unknown moment M_A at A, as shown in Fig. 104c. The equation of compatibility in this case is that, for the case in Fig. 104c to return to the case of the propped cantilever, the clockwise slope caused by the uniformly distributed load must be exactly equal and opposite to the anti-clockwise slope caused by the moment M_A so that when the loadings are combined, the final slope at the end A is zero and the end A returns to being a fixed end. Referring again to Fig. 84 for the slopes we have,

$$\frac{wL^3}{24EI} = \frac{M_AL}{3EI}$$

which gives

$$M_A = \frac{wL^2}{8} = \frac{WL}{8} \text{---} 48$$

The bending moment diagram in this case can be drawn by superimposing the bending moment diagram for the simply supported beam under a uniformly distributed load (which is a parabola as we have seen in Example

3.7.1 and shown in Fig. 28) on the bending moment diagram for the simply supported beam with a moment $\mathbf{M_A}$ applied at one end (which is a simple triangle of opposite sign) to yield the final bending moment diagram shown in Fig. 105a.

The bending moment and shear force diagrams in Fig. 105 are of considerable interest and a great deal can be learnt from them. The bending moment changes sign at $\mathbf{C}$ and such a point is called a point of **contraflexure** or point of **inflection** because on referring to the deflection diagram for the propped cantilever shown dotted in Fig. 104a, it is seen that the same point $\mathbf{C}$ defines a change in curvature as well. At the point $\mathbf{C}$, the curvature changes from a **hogging** curvature on the left to a **sagging** curvature on the right. The bending moment at a point of contraflexure is always zero. The bending moment at a pin or a hinge is also always zero as we have seen in our discussion of support end conditions in 3.6 and shown in Fig. 27b. This means that the presence of a pin could be assumed at a point of contraflexure, such as $\mathbf{C}$, without changing the structural behavior of the beam in any way. This is an important concept and will be used extensively in our study of more complex indeterminate systems such as portal frames.

It can further be seen in Fig. 105a that the maximum positive moment occurs at $\mathbf{D}$ at which point the shear force is zero. This enables us in fact to determine the position of maximum positive moment by determining the point at which the shear force is zero. In this case it is the point $\mathbf{D}$. Once the position of $\mathbf{D}$ is fixed, the moment at $\mathbf{D}$ can then be easily calculated.

It may also be noted that the sign convention relating negative moment to a hogging curvature and positive moment to a sagging curvature is arbitrary. What is not arbitrary however, is the fact that the moment between $\mathbf{A}$ and $\mathbf{C}$ causes tension to occur on the top fibers of the beam whereas the moment between $\mathbf{C}$ and $\mathbf{B}$ causes tension to occur on the bottom fibers of the beam. This is important because in a reinforced concrete beam it would be necessary to put the main longitudinal steel reinforcement on the tensile side of the beam. In the case of the propped cantilever under vertical load as shown in Fig. 104a, the main steel would run at the top of the beam in the region $\mathbf{A}$ to $\mathbf{C}$ and would then have to be bent down to run at the bottom of the beam in the region $\mathbf{C}$ to $\mathbf{B}$. Separate reinforcement without bent up bars could of course be provided in the two regions and be perfectly acceptable.

The fixed end beam is shown in Fig. 106, subjected to a uniformly distributed load as shown in Fig. 106a and a point load $\mathbf{W}$ placed anywhere on the beam as in Fig. 106b. The analysis of the fixed end beam follows the same pattern as for the propped cantilever but the equations of compatibility in this case require that the slopes at the ends $\mathbf{A}$ and $\mathbf{B}$ of the beam must both be equal to zero. The deflection diagrams are shown dotted in Fig. 106 and the points of contraflexure have been defined. The bending moment dia-

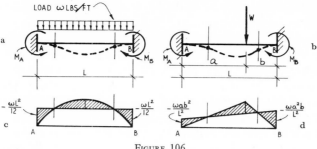

FIGURE 106

grams for the beams show once again that the bending moment at the points of contraflexure is zero.

The Architect is not really required to solve each particular case since all cases for various types of beams have already been fully solved and are readily available for reference. Any good structural engineering handbook or reference design manual will list a large number of cases of single span statically indeterminate beams under a variety of loadings.

7.3 Continuous beams

All beams need not be single span beams. Sometimes it is advantageous to run the beam continuous over two or more spans. The effect of continuity over the supports is to cause a partial fixity with a change in curvature from sagging in the center section of the spans (under vertical downward loading) to hogging over the supports, except at the end supports where the curvature depends on whether the end support is simply supported or fixed. The effect of continuity over the supports is therefore to change the sign of the moment as it passes over the support thereby lowering the maximum design moments and providing more even distribution of moments over the beam. A two span continuous beam under uniformly distributed loading is shown in Fig. 107. It may be seen that due to perfect symmetry, the slope of the beam over the support **B** has to be zero thereby making each span into a propped cantilever. The bending moment diagram

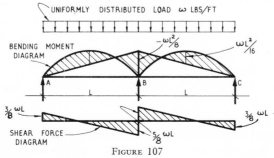

FIGURE 107

and the shear force diagram, for the beam shown in Fig. 107, are the same as for two propped cantilevers.

Once again it is not necessary for the Architect to be able to analyse every case of continuous beam since a large number of cases for different numbers of spans and under a variety of loadings have been already solved and are readily available for reference in structural design handbooks or manuals. The bending moment and shear force diagrams given in such books may be used with confidence.

For reinforced concrete design, the ACI Code 318-71 gives the values of bending moments and shear forces that may be used in the design of continuous beams under a uniformly distributed load of **w** lbs/ft and modified values have been given in Table 7.3.1.

Table 7.3.1
COEFFICIENTS FOR CONTINUOUS REINFORCED CONCRETE BEAMS

Bending moments

Positive moment in end span .... $+ \dfrac{1}{11} \, \mathbf{wL}^2$

Positive moment all interior spans .... $+ \dfrac{1}{16} \, \mathbf{wL}^2$

Negative moment at first interior support

    Two spans only .... $- \dfrac{1}{9} \, \mathbf{wL}^2$

    More than two spans .... $- \dfrac{1}{10} \, \mathbf{wL}^2$

Negative moment all other interior supports .... $- \dfrac{1}{11} \, \mathbf{wL}^2$

Shear force

Shear in end span at first interior support .... $1.15 \, \dfrac{\mathbf{wL}}{2}$

Shear at all other supports .... $\dfrac{\mathbf{wL}}{2}$

Example 7.3.1

A reinforced concrete three span continuous beam is shown diagrammatically in Fig. 108. Use the concrete coefficients of Table 7.3.1 to deter-

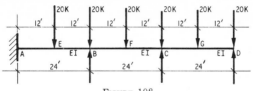

FIGURE 108

mine **approximately** the bending moments and shear forces in the beam for purposes of design. The dead load of the beam itself is 250 lbs/ft.

The coefficients in Table 7.3.1 have been given for uniformly distributed loads on the beam. The dead load of the beam of 0.25 K/ft is uniformly distributed, but the major loads of 20 K each unfortunately are point loads. The point loads over the supports **B**, **C** and **D** are transmitted directly into the columns and do not enter into the calculations for the analysis of the beam. The 20 K loads at **E**, **F** and **G** may be assumed to be uniformly distributed over each span but of a value equal to 40 K. The justification for this approximation is that the maximum positive moments for a simply supported span would then be the same, as follows:

For a point load $\mathbf{W'}$, $\mathbf{BM} = \dfrac{\mathbf{W'L}}{4}$

For a uniformly distributed load $\mathbf{W''}$, $\mathbf{BM} = \dfrac{\mathbf{W''L}}{8}$

For these maximum moments to be equal therefore $\mathbf{W''} = 2\mathbf{W'}$

The total uniformly distributed load per ft of beam is approximately therefore,

$$\mathbf{w} = \frac{40}{24} + 0.25 = 1.67 + 0.25 = 1.92 \text{ K/ft}$$

Using the coefficients as given in Table 7.3.1 we have,

Negative moment at $\mathbf{D} = 0$

Negative moment at $\mathbf{C} = -\dfrac{1}{10}\,\mathbf{w}\mathbf{L}^2 = -\dfrac{1}{10} \times 1.92 \times 24^2 = -110.6$ K ft

Negative moment at $\mathbf{B} = -\dfrac{1}{11}\,\mathbf{w}\mathbf{L}^2 = -\dfrac{1}{11} \times 1.92 \times 24^2 = -100.5$ K ft

Negative moment at $\mathbf{A} = -\dfrac{1}{16}\,\mathbf{w}\mathbf{L}^2 = -\dfrac{1}{16} \times 1.92 \times 24^2 = -69.1$ K ft

Positive moment at $\mathbf{G} = +\dfrac{1}{11}\,\mathbf{w}\mathbf{L}^2 = +\dfrac{1}{11} \times 1.92 \times 24^2 = +100.5$ K ft

Positive moment at **F**

$$\text{and at } \mathbf{E} = +\frac{1}{16}\,\mathbf{wL}^2 = +\frac{1}{16} \times 1.92 \times 24^2 = +69.1 \text{ K ft}$$

$$\text{Shear force at } \mathbf{C} = 1.15\,\frac{\mathbf{wL}}{2} = 1.15 \times \frac{1.92 \times 24}{2} = 26.5 \text{ K}$$

$$\text{Shear force at } \mathbf{B} \text{ and at } \mathbf{A} = \frac{\mathbf{wL}}{2} = \frac{1.92 \times 24}{2} = 23 \text{ K}$$

The bending moment diagram for the beam can now be easily drawn and has been shown in Fig. 109a. The negative moments are once again over the supports. The exact bending moment diagram theoretically calculated

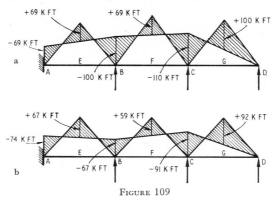

FIGURE 109

and without any approximation concerning the nature of the load is shown in Fig. 109b. It can be seen that in the maximum moments (which are the design moments for calculating the size of the beam) the differences are small. The approximations made and the use of the coefficients in Table 7.3.1 have yielded a slightly safer design than is actually necessary by theoretical analysis.

7.4 Portal frames

A portal frame is a statically indeterminate structure in which the beam does not merely rest on the column but is rigidly connected to it. The result is that the column affords partial fixity to the beam creating negative moments at the ends of the beam and thereby providing for a more even distribution of moment. The maximum positive moments in the beam are considerably reduced. The columns are now required to carry moments as well and this leads to a more uniform section for beam and column members. The rigid connections are very important to portal or rigid frame action and a typical rigid connection between the beam and column member of a rectangular portal frame in steel is shown in Fig. 110.

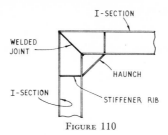

FIGURE 110

Portal frames can be in steel, concrete or timber. They can be rectangular or with a pitched roof as shown in Fig. 2b. They can be single bay, single storey or multi-bay, multi-storey in construction. A single bay, two storey portal frame in concrete is shown in Fig. 17, whilst a two bay, six storey portal frame in steel has been shown in Fig. 10a. A portal frame in timber also goes by the name of **tudor arch** and has been shown in Fig. 118e.

The feet of the portal or rigid frame can be either pinned or fixed. With pinned feet, the moment at the pins is zero as we have seen and the column section can be tapered, if it is economical to do so, as in concrete or glued laminated timber. With fixed feet, the moments at the feet have to be transferred into the foundations (in addition to the vertical and horizontal forces) and the foundations themselves have to be designed to withstand these forces and moments and dissipate them safely into the soil without soil failure or settlement.

Finally it may be noted that if the portal frame, in addition to pins at the feet also has a third pin, at the center of the beam in a rectangular portal frame or at the crown as in a pitched roof portal frame, the structure is statically determinate and can be analysed using exactly the same principles as were discussed for the three pin arch considered in 3.9.

7.5 Approximate analysis of simple portal frames

Rectangular portal frames are shown in Fig. 111. The frame shown in Fig. 111a cannot sway sideways even under the horizontal load **W** because the beam member transmits the load directly into the shear wall to which the frame is attached. Frames such as this, which cannot sway, are also sometimes called **portal bents**. A true rectangular portal frame is shown in Fig. 111b, but the structure shown cannot sway either under the loading shown. The structure is symmetrical and since the load is symmetrical as well, no sway can take place. The portal frames shown in Figs. 111c, d and e are all subject to sway. The frame in Fig. 111e sways because of the horizontal load and this sway is easy to visualise. The frames shown in Figs. 111c and d however, sway because the structure is not perfectly symmetrical. In Fig. 111c, the non-symmetry arises out of the boundary conditions as one base is fixed and the other is pinned. In Fig. 111d, the non-symmetry arises out of the different sizes and hence stiffnesses of the column members.

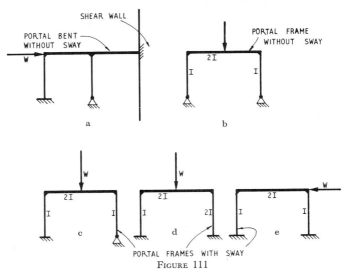

FIGURE 111

Consider a simple rectangular portal frame under a horizontal load **W** (such as may be caused by wind) and shown in Fig. 112a. The deflected shape of the frame is shown dotted and grossly exaggerated in Fig. 112a. As can be seen the structure develops three points of contraflexure or inflection. At such points the curvature changes from one side to the other and the bending moment at these points is zero. In effect therefore, such a point in the structure functions as a pin. If it were possible therefore to approximately determine the position of these points of contraflexure, pins could be inserted into the structure at these points without affecting its structural behavior—but making it much simpler to analyse, because it has now reduced to a statically determinate structure. If the position of the point of contraflexure is only approximately correct, the final bending moments obtained are also only approximately correct—but are still good enough for purposes of design.

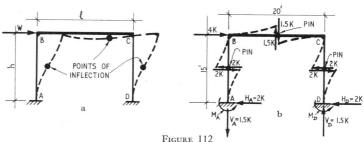

FIGURE 112

The analysis of the fixed base portal frame shown in Fig. 112a will therefore be carried out on the assumption that the points of contraflexure occur at the centers of the beam and the columns and by inserting physical pins into the structure at these points. The structure is now statically determinate and can be analysed by the simple rules of statics as will be seen by an example taken here.

Example 7.5.1

Draw the approximate bending moment diagram for the single bay, single storey, fixed base portal frame shown in Fig. 112b under a horizontal load of 4 K at **B**.

As has been previously stated, the points of contraflexure are assumed to occur at the centers of the beam and the columns and since the bending moment is zero at these points pins are inserted into the structure at these points **E**, **F** and **G**. The upper and lower parts of the portal frame can now be separated as shown in Figs. 113 and 114. Consider the upper part shown in Fig. 113. Taking moments for the upper part about **E** we have,

$$V_G \times 20 - 4 \times 7.5 = 0$$

$$V_G = 1.5\ K$$

For vertical equilibrium,

$$V_E = V_G = 1.5\ K$$

The directions of the vertical forces are shown in Fig. 113. In order to

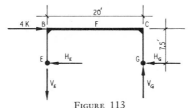

FIGURE 113

determine the horizontal force **H**$_G$ consider half of the upper part as shown in Fig. 114a and take moments about **F**. We have for rotational equilibrium,

$$V_G \times 10 - H_G \times 7.5 = 0$$

$$H_G \times 7.5 = 1.5 \times 10 = 15$$

$$H_G = 2\ K$$

By considering again the whole of the upper part shown in Fig. 113 and taking horizontal equilibrium we have,

$$H_G + H_E = 4$$

This gives **H**$_E$ = **H**$_G$ = 2 K which could have been written down by inspection without difficulty. Finally the vertical shear **V**$_F$ at **F** can be written

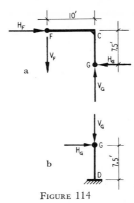

FIGURE 114

down by inspection as 1.5 K since, as may be seen in Fig. 114a, it must be equal to V_G to maintain vertical equilibrium. The lower parts of the frame are simple cantilevers and the portion **GD** is shown in Fig. 114b.

All these forces can be transferred back to the portal frame as shown in Fig. 112b and the bending moments for all the individual parts of the beam or the columns, considered as simple cantilevers, can readily be obtained. The bending moment at **D** for instance, is $2 \times 7.5 = 15$ K ft. The bending moment at **B** in the beam is $1.5 \times 10 = 15$ K ft. The bending moment diagram has been shown in Fig. 115.

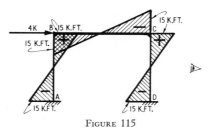

FIGURE 115

It may be noted that this bending moment diagram is only approximately correct because the positions of the points of inflection were assumed at the center of the beam and the columns.

The problem taken in Example 7.5.1 had fixed feet. If the portal frame is a pinned base portal frame with real pins at the feet, then there is only one point of contraflexure at the center of the beam. The deflected shape for such a portal frame (shown grossly exaggerated) is given by the dotted lines in Fig. 116.

The use of this method of analysis and a further study of the load propagation through multi-bay, multi-storey rigid frames for high rise buildings will be made in Chapter 8.

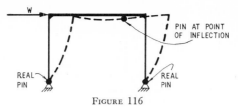

FIGURE 116

7.6 Arches

The three pin arch is statically determinate and has been considered in 3.9. If the pin at the crown is eliminated, the arch becomes a **two pin arch** with pins only at the feet and is statically indeterminate. The two pin arch can be built in steel, concrete or timber though steel is not a favored material unless the arch can be built as a trussed arch as shown in Fig. 117. Poured

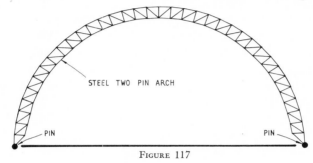

FIGURE 117

in place concrete presents no difficulty in arch construction, though the formwork in which the concrete is poured has to be supported whilst the concrete is curing and could be expensive. Timber glued laminated arches are quite convenient to use and come in a variety of shapes shown in Fig. 118.

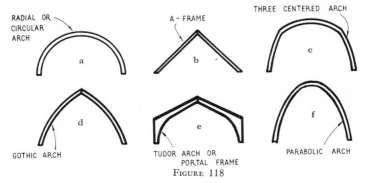

FIGURE 118

All two pin arches have pins at the feet and so the moment at the feet is zero. The pins however transmit vertical and horizontal forces to the foundations and these have to be resisted by the foundations. The vertical forces can be easily resisted by soil pressure but to resist the horizontal thrusts requires the provision of buttresses or horizontal ties, as was discussed in 3.9 and shown in Fig. 41.

Fixed arches, as their name implies, have fixed feet and large moments therefore develop at the feet of the arch. This makes the section of the arch large at the base and decreasing towards the crown. One disadvantage of fixed arches is that the moments at the feet have to be resisted by the foundations without rotation. This tends to make the foundations massive and expensive.

The analysis of two pin and fixed arches, both circular and parabolic in shape, under a wide variety of loadings has been well documented and the maximum bending moments, shear forces and axial thrusts for an accurate design can be readily obtained from **Arches—Tables for Statical Analysis** published by the Pergamon Press.

The overall dimensioning of the arch, discussed for three pin arches in 3.9 apply to two pin and fixed arches as well, but these latter arches can be shallower than the three pin type if necessary.

Problems for solution

Example 1: With the help of Reference books in the library, determine the maximum negative moments for the beam shown in Fig. 29—but with the ends **A** and **E** fully fixed.

Hint: Take each load separately and add the cases together.

Ans: $M_A = -15.51$ K ft, $M_E = -14.77$ K ft.

Example 2: Draw the bending moment and shear force diagram for a propped cantilever of span **L** with a central point load **W**.

Ans: M_{max} negative at the fixed end $= -\dfrac{3}{16}$ **WL**

M_{max} positive at the center $= +\dfrac{5}{32}$ **WL**

Example 3: Use the coefficients for continuous beams in concrete, to determine the maximum negative and positive design moments for the two span beam under uniformly distributed loading shown in Fig. 107.

Ans: Positive design moment $= +\dfrac{1}{11}$ **wL²**

Negative design moment over the center support $= -\dfrac{1}{9}$ **wL²**

Example 4: Draw the bending moment diagram for the two pin rigid rectangular portal frame shown in Fig. 116, under the horizontal load. Span of the beam member = 20 ft, height of column member = 15 ft, **W** = 4 K.

Ans: Maximum moment at the knees = 30 K ft.

Example 5: A two pin parabolic arch under a uniformly distributed load is shown in Fig. 119. Use the literature available in the library to determine the horizontal thrust **H** at the feet of the arch.

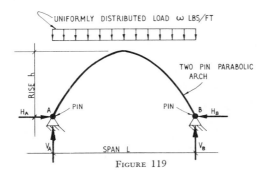

FIGURE 119

Example 6: A fixed parabolic arch is shown in Fig. 120a and a fixed circular arch is shown in Fig. 120b. Use the literature available in the library to determine the horizontal thrust **H**, vertical reaction **V** and moments **M** at the feet of the arches. Make any necessary assumptions.

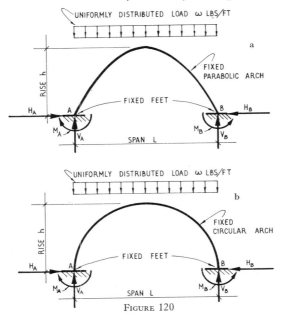

FIGURE 120

Example 7: The tudor arch shown in Fig. 118e is available pre-engineered in structural glued laminated timber. Such an arch is to be used with the following data:

$$\text{Span } \mathbf{L} = 60 \text{ ft}$$

$$\text{Total rise } \mathbf{h} = 25 \text{ ft}$$

$$\text{Wall height} = 17.5 \text{ ft}$$

$$\text{Spacing} = 16 \text{ ft}$$

$$\text{Roof pitch} = 3/12$$

$$\text{Total load (dead} + \text{snow)} = 45 \text{ lbs/sq ft}$$

Use Handbooks or Trade literature to determine the approximate size of the tudor arch and detail the structure.

Ans: 6¾ in. × 24 in. section, 12 in. depth at crown, 15¾ in. depth at feet.

Chapter 8
HIGH RISE STRUCTURES

8.1 High rise structures

The term high rise structures covers a number of different types of buildings with sometimes vastly differing architectural and structural arrangements. They have only one feature in common and that is that they are tall buildings, which due to restricted and expensive site conditions have a considerable amount of vertical development above the ground. This implies therefore that they must have an efficient vertical transportation system of elevators, stairs, fire escapes, etc. Since there are a large number of storeys, it also follows that the floor arrangements for all storeys particularly in the **tower** block will be identical in layout. This is essential because a change in the layout of the floor, involving changes in the positions of the elevators in the tower block, would not be easily possible. Certain modifications are easily possible in the lobby area, where columns may be cut off to provide column free spaces as shown in Fig. 121. The load from the internal columns

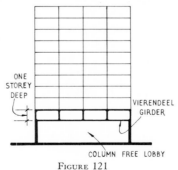

FIGURE 121

is transferred to the columns at the ends by the use of heavy floor trusses. If diagonals are objectionable, **vierendeel girders** or open trusses with rigid joints may be used, with a structural depth that is one full storey deep. The vierendeel girder must have fully rigid joints for stability and is shown again in Fig. 122. In the very end bays, trusses with diagonals and one storey deep, as shown in Fig. 33, can of course be used.

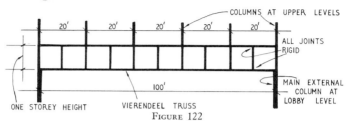

FIGURE 122

The most important factor from the point of view of the structure however, is not the layout, but the nature of the horizontal wind and earthquake loading and the manner in which this loading is to be taken by the structure and safely transmitted to the foundations. This loading becomes the most critical one because of the height of the building.

The horizontal loads on a multi-storey high rise building can be provided for by a number of different alternative structural arrangements as follows:

a. Simple frames with bracing
b. Rigid frames
c. Concrete shear walls or service cores with columns
d. Concrete central core with cantilevered floors
e. Concrete load bearing walls.

8.2 Simple frames with bracing

This is the simplest type of structural arrangement with beams simply supported on columns and without rigid joints as shown in Fig. 123. It is suitable for steel but not very suitable for concrete. The wind loading on the

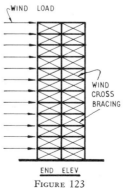

FIGURE 123

structure causes **racking** and so to prevent collapse, a system of bracing has to be introduced as shown in Fig. 123.

The purpose of bracing and the manner in which it functions is shown in Fig. 124. Under the horizontal load, the original rectangular shape of the

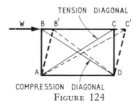

FIGURE 124

frame **ABCD** deforms and tends to elongate one diagonal **AC** to **AC′** and shorten the other diagonal **BD** to **B′D**. This is shown exaggerated in Fig. 124. If the elongation in the diagonal **AC** were to be resisted by the insertion of a tension brace (a steel angle or a tie rod) the racking of the frame is prevented and it is made stable. In fact the triangulation that was discussed in Chapter 3 in 3.8, has taken place giving rise to a stable structure. If now the wind were to blow the other way, the diagonal **AC** is no longer in tension but is in compression. Since the brace **AC** is a slender member, it is efficient in tension but would buckle in compression and be ineffective. The other diagonal **BD** hence also needs to be inserted for wind in the opposite direction. This leads to **cross bracing** as shown in Fig. 123.

It can be seen that cross bracing has one serious disadvantage in that it can obstruct the flow through the spaces of the building. For internal frames there are alternative bracing arrangements and one such type is shown in Fig. 125. If bracing in internal bays is totally unacceptable, but heavy wind

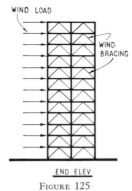

FIGURE 125

bracing in the external frames is acceptable, a rigid floor system or horizontal bracing should be provided at every floor level. The floor then acts as a rigid horizontal truss or girder, takes the wind loads from the internal bays and transmits them horizontally to the end frames which are braced and which then carry all the wind loads. This is shown in Fig. 126.

Finally it should be noted that to transfer the wind shears into the columns requires, in any case, a fairly rigid floor system and so horizontal floor bracing at each floor level may sometimes be necessary.

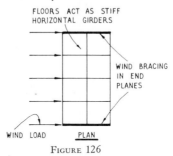

FIGURE 126

The design of bracing for a simple structure will now be considered.

Example 8.2.1

A simple frame structure shown in Fig. 127 is acted upon by a wind load of 30 lbs/sq ft on a vertical surface. If internal wind bracing is not to be permitted, design the wind bracing in external frames.

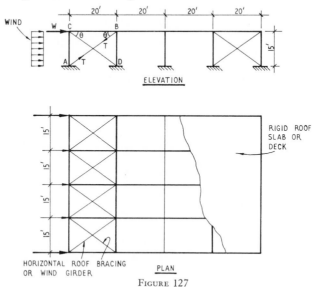

FIGURE 127

It is assumed that the roof is sufficiently rigid to transfer the wind forces acting on internal frames to the external ones. With a total coefficient C_D

for windward and leeward sides of 1.4, the total horizontal force at the top of the building can be obtained as,

$$\mathbf{W'} = 30 \times 1.4 \times 60 \times 15 \times \frac{1}{2} = 18900 \text{ lbs}$$

The wind load on each frame is hence,

$$\mathbf{W''} = \frac{18900}{2} = 9450 \text{ lbs}$$

The load is further assumed to be taken along the side of the end frames by the bracings in the two corner panels only. The internal panels, even in the end frames, can be free of bracing as shown in Fig. 127. The load therefore in any one panel and on any one set of braces is,

$$\mathbf{W} = \frac{9450}{2} = 4725 \text{ lbs}$$

The compression diagonal is assumed to be ineffective and the load in the tension diagonal **AB** can be obtained by considering the horizontal equilibrium of the joint **B.** This gives,

$$\mathbf{W} = \mathbf{T} \, \mathbf{Cos} \, \theta = \mathbf{T} \times \frac{20}{25}$$

$$4725 = \mathbf{T} \times 0.80$$

$$\mathbf{T} = \frac{4725}{0.80} = 5906 \text{ lbs}$$

Use an A36 single angle 2 in. $\times$ 2 in. $\times$ $\frac{1}{4}$ in. thick, gross area = 0.94 sq in. Net area with $\frac{5}{8}$ in. diameter bolts in $\frac{3}{4}$ in. diameter holes is,

$$\mathbf{A} = 0.94 - \frac{3}{4} \times \frac{1}{4} = 0.94 - 0.19 = 0.75 \text{ sq in.}$$

The axial tensile stress can hence be calculated by Eqn. 12 as,

$$\mathbf{t} = \frac{\mathbf{T}}{\mathbf{A}} = \frac{5906}{0.75} = 7875 \text{ psi}$$

Since this is much less than the 22000 psi permitted in axial tension for A36 steel, the section is acceptable.

Provide cross bracing with 2 in. $\times$ 2 in. $\times$ $\frac{1}{4}$ in. single angle in all corner bays on all sides of the building. If round bar bracing is used it can be shown that a $\frac{3}{4}$ in. diameter round bar would be sufficient, but a turnbuckle should be provided to tighten up the structure. Proper bracing is very important to the safety of the structure and a little overdesign in the sections chosen is not objectionable.

8.3 **Rigid frames**

If wind bracing is considered as architecturally objectionable, the structure can be constructed with rigid joints. It is then a rigid frame high rise structure of the type shown in Fig. 10a. This form of construction is very suitable with steel, where the joints between the beams and the columns can be welded, or with concrete where they can be cast monolithically. Haunches can also be provided as shown in Figs. 17 and 110.

Consider the three bay, ten storey rigid frame high rise structure shown in Fig. 128 subjected to wind loads. The analysis of the structure, under the

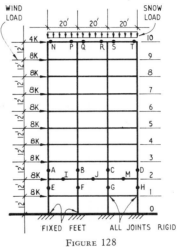

FIGURE 128

horizontal loads, can be carried out by using the same approach as was used for simple portal frames in 7.5. This method requires that pins be inserted into the structure at the assumed positions of the points of contraflexure, thereby considerably simplifying the analysis of the structure by reducing it to a statically determinate one. For a multi-bay, multi-storey rigid frame of the type shown in Fig. 128, the following assumptions can be made:

a. There is a point of contraflexure at the mid-height of each column.
b. There is a point of contraflexure at the center of each beam.
c. Each bay acts as a simple portal. The total horizontal load at each storey level is divided between the bays in proportion to the spans. The vertical forces are taken only by the external columns.

The analysis of the structure can be easily carried out at any desired storey level and will be illustrated by an example.

Example 8.3.1

Draw the bending moment diagram at the second storey level for the rigid frame high rise structure shown in Fig. 128.

Under the assumptions **a** and **b** of 8.3, pins can be inserted into the structure at **A, B, C, D, E, F, G, H, I, J** and **M**. This has been shown in Fig. 128. The entire second storey can then be removed from the structure and treated as a free body provided the forces are reintroduced at the pins.

Consider the horizontal shear at the level of **A, B, C** and **D**.

$$\text{Total horizontal shear} = 4 + 8 \times 7 = 4 + 56 = 60 \text{ K}$$

Under the assumption **c** this horizontal shear is divided in the ratio of the spans and so each bay takes 20 K. As we have seen in Example 7.5.1, the horizontal force at the feet of each bay considered as a separate portal is 10 K. Since however, **B** and **C** have horizontal forces from two bays, the total horizontal shear on these pins is 20 K. The horizontal forces at the level of **A, B, C** and **D** are shown in Fig. 129.

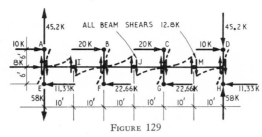

FIGURE 129

Similarly the total horizontal shear at the level of **E, F, G** and **H** can be got as 68 K and can be divided into horizontal forces of 11.33 K at **E** and **H** and 22.66 K at the internal pins **F** and **G**.

The directions of the forces at both levels should be noted. In both cases, we are concerned only with the forces that the rest of the structure imposes on the second storey level, which is being considered as the free body. The forces on the upper pins are therefore to the right whilst the forces on the lower pins are to the left.

In order to determine the vertical forces in the external columns (internal columns do not take vertical forces under wind load according to assumption **c**) it is necessary to consider the moment or rotational equilibrium of the entire structure at the level of the pins. Taking moments for all the forces above the level of **A, B, C** and **D** about **A** we have,

$$4 \times 90 + 8 \times (78 + 66 + 54 + 42 + 30 + 18 + 6) = \mathbf{V_D} \times 60$$

$$\mathbf{V_D} = \frac{2712}{60} = 45.2 \text{ K}$$

Once again we are interested in the forces that the rest of the structure, above the second storey level, imposes on the pins **A** and **D** and hence the vertical force at **D** is downward. For vertical equilibrium therefore, the force at **A** is upward and equal to 45.2 K.

To determine the vertical forces at **E** and **H**, the moment or rotational equilibrium of the superstructure (including the second storey) can similarly be considered and taking moments about **E** we have,

$$4 \times 102 + 8 \times (90 + 78 + 66 + 54 + 42 + 30 + 18 + 6) = \mathbf{V_H} \times 60$$

$$\mathbf{V_H} = \frac{3480}{60} = 58.0 \text{ K}$$

In this case again, we require the vertical forces that the lower part of the structure imposes on the second storey and so the direction of the vertical force on the pin at **H** is upwards. For vertical equilibrium, the vertical force at **E** is downwards and equal to 58.0 K. All these vertical forces have been shown in Fig. 129.

It now only remains for the shears in the beams to be determined for the analysis to be complete. Consider the vertical equilibrium of the column **AE** separated from the rest of the second storey and considered as a free body. It can be seen that the vertical forces at **A** and **E** are not balanced. The beam therefore must impose a force on the column to keep the column in vertical equilibrium—and this is the shear in the beam.

$$\text{Shear in the beam} = 58.0 - 45.2 = 12.8 \text{ K}$$

The force of the beam on the column must be upwards and so the force of the column on the beam must be downwards. The shear in all parts of the beam is constant and the shears have been shown in Fig. 129. As a check, the vertical equilibrium of the column **DH** may be considered to ensure that the directions of the shears are correct.

The bending moments for each part of beam or column can now be determined, as in Example 7.5.1, by considering each part to be a simple cantilever fixed at the joints. This gives the maximum moments as,

$$\mathbf{BM}_{max} \text{ in all beams} = 12.8 \times 10 = 128 \text{ K ft}$$

$$\mathbf{BM}_{max} \text{ in external columns above the second storey level} =$$
$$10 \times 6 = 60 \text{ K ft}$$

$$\mathbf{BM}_{max} \text{ in internal columns above the second storey level} =$$
$$20 \times 6 = 120 \text{ K ft}$$

$$\mathbf{BM}_{max} \text{ in external columns below the second storey level} =$$
$$11.33 \times 6 = 68 \text{ K ft}$$

$$\mathbf{BM}_{max} \text{ in internal columns below the second storey level} =$$
$$22.66 \times 6 = 136 \text{ K ft}$$

The bending moment diagram for the entire second storey has been shown in Fig. 130.

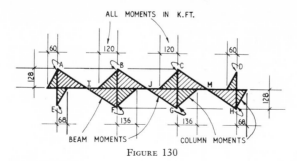

FIGURE 130

8.4 Concrete shear walls or service cores with columns

In this type of construction, all the wind or earthquake forces are transferred by the floor system into rigid vertical **shear walls** which run the entire height of the building. These shear walls can form a **service core** housing the elevators and stairs, as shown in Fig. 10b, or they can be placed at the ends of the building. In both cases however, the remainder of the slender columns are tied to the massive, heavily reinforced concrete walls by the floor system. Though the shear walls run continuously through the building, they can be punctured without difficulty for the provision of elevator doors, mechanical services, etc. The analysis and design of shear walls is very complex and will not be considered here. It is useful for the Architect to know that the thickness of these walls can range from 1 ft to 2 ft 6 in. or more depending on the height of the high rise structure.

8.5 Concrete central core with cantilevered floors

In some restricted site conditions, it may not be easily possible to provide adequate foundations for external columns. In such circumstances a useful, though expensive, method of high rise construction can be carried out with a massive central concrete core with cantilevered floors as shown in Fig. 131a. The concrete core runs through the entire height of the building and takes both horizontal loads due to the wind as also all the vertical loads from the floors, as a free standing cantilever. The concrete core at the top has a massive double cantilevered truss system as shown in Fig. 131a. Each main floor beam is anchored into the core at one end and is supported by a tension hanger at the other.

It is useful to verbalise the load propagation through the structural system. The main floor beams are propped cantilevers which load the core at one end, the prop reaction being taken by the hanger. The hangers collect the vertical load from all the floor beams and carry the load upwards to the cantilever roof truss system at the top of the core. The cantilever roof truss system then reintroduces the loads into the core at the top which then transmits the loads to the foundations. The horizontal forces due to wind are

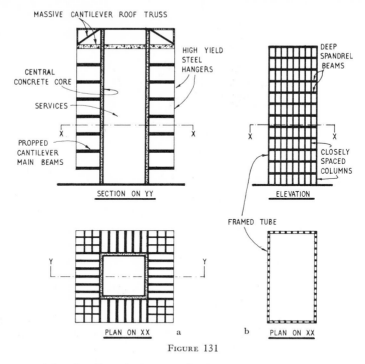

FIGURE 131

transmitted by the floor beams to the core and are then taken directly by the core.

The design of the tension hanger for such a system is fairly simple as will be seen by an example taken here.

Example 8.5.1

Design the tension hanger for the high rise structure shown in Fig. 131a with the following data:

Plan dimensions of building = 64 ft × 64 ft

Plan dimensions of concrete core = 32 ft × 32 ft

Number of storeys = 8

Storey height = 12 ft

Live load on each storey = 100 lbs/sq ft

Dead load on each storey = 100 lbs/sq ft

Spacing of the floor beams = 5 ft 4 in.

Material of the hanger = A441 steel (high tensile steel)

Determine also the maximum elongation of the hanger.

The span of each main beam is 16 ft. The load on each main beam is therefore,

$$W' = 200 \times 5.33 \times 16 = 17056 \text{ lbs}$$

The beams are propped cantilevers, anchored into the core at one end and propped by the hangers. Referring to the analysis of the propped cantilever in 7.2, it is seen that the reaction on the prop is $\frac{3}{8} W'$.

Load in the hanger from each floor $= \frac{3}{8} W' = \frac{3}{8} \times 17056 = 6396 \text{ lbs}$

The hanger collects load from all the floors and carries it to the top and so the total maximum load on each hanger is,

$$W = 6396 \times 7 = 44772 \text{ lbs}$$

The permissible stress in A441 steel, from Table 4.1.1, is 30 ksi. The cross sectional area of the hanger can therefore be obtained as,

$$A = \frac{\textbf{Force in hanger}}{\textbf{permissible stress}} = \frac{44772}{30000} = 1.49 \text{ sq in.}$$

Use a hanger 6 in. $\times \frac{3}{8}$ in., area $= 2.25$ sq in.

If the same section of the hanger is maintained throughout the height of the building, the tip elongation at the first storey is the sum of the elongations of the individual sections of the hanger. The elongation of a tension member, by Eqn. 18 is,

$$\delta L = \frac{TL}{AE}$$

Where $E = 30 \times 10^6$ psi and $L = 12$ ft. The elongations can hence be got as,

$$\delta L_1 = \frac{6396 \times 144}{2.25 \times 30 \times 10^6} = 0.014 \text{ in.}$$

$$\delta L_2 = \frac{6396 \times 2 \times 144}{2.25 \times 30 \times 10^6} = 0.028 \text{ in.}$$

It can be seen that the elongations in the individual lengths increase in the same proportion as the build up of load in the hanger and so the total elongation of the hanger can be calculated as,

$$\delta L_T = 0.014 \, (1 + 2 + 3 + 4 + 5 + 6 + 7) = 0.014 \times 28 = 0.39 \text{ in.}$$

8.6 Concrete load bearing walls

The concrete shear walls or service cores considered in 8.4 and 8.5 are necessarily poured in place because of their massive nature. Another form of concrete wall construction, using prefabricated wall and floor elements, is possible for high rise concrete buildings between five and eighteen storeys high. Such construction is shown in Fig. 132. The wall and floor elements,

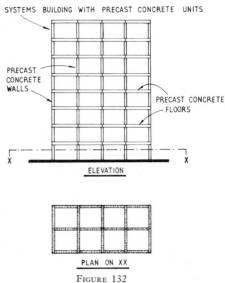

FIGURE 132

about 6 in. thick, are precast in a factory and transported to site where they are erected in a predetermined pattern with joints that are partly mechanical and partly poured in place. The whole building then rises like a house of cards. The analogy points out an inherent weakness of this form of construction if the jointing is inadequate and it is therefore imperative that the joints between wall and wall and between wall and floor are properly designed and constructed. With adequate jointing however, the system is very rapid in construction and could hence be economical to the client.

8.7 Behavior as a tube

A more modern approach to the design of rigid frame high rise structures or multi-storey buildings is to consider the entire structure as a **framed tube**. This is shown in Fig. 131b. In this approach, the external columns are very closely spaced and are properly tied by deep spandrel beams in order to force the entire structure to behave as a framed tube. For a large building, a number of such tubes can be considered as acting together in a bundle and each may then be cut off at the desired height.

Problems for solution

Example 1: A single bay, two storey portal frame is shown in Fig. 17.

The wind loads on the portal have been determined in Example 1 in the problems for solution at the end of Chapter 2. Draw the bending moment diagram for the frame with fixed feet. It may be assumed that the beam members are stiff enough for the wind load at **A** and **B** to be considered as acting at **A** and for the wind load at **C** and **D** to be considered as acting at **C**.

Ans: BM$_A$ = BM$_B$ = 14040 lb ft, **BM** at the feet = 42120 lb ft.

Example 2: The roof of the high rise rigid frame structure of Fig. 128 is subjected to snow load as shown in Fig. 133a. Assuming the positions of the points of inflection as shown, determine the design positive and negative moments in the center beam.

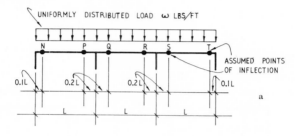

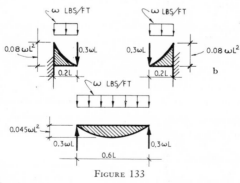

FIGURE 133

Ans: Fig. 133b.

Example 3: If the concrete core in Example 8.5.1 is only 24 ft × 24 ft and if the main central beams are spaced at 8 ft on centers, calculate the size of the high tensile steel hanger for the structure.

Ans: 2.8 sq in. Say 8 in. × ⅜ in.

Chapter 9

GRIDS AND SLABS

9.1 The grid structure

A grid structure consists of a number of beams interconnected at the points of intersection as shown in Fig. 134. Such a structure is more efficient

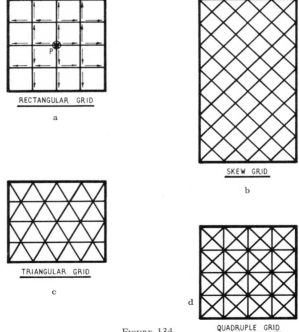

RECTANGULAR GRID

a

SKEW GRID

b

TRIANGULAR GRID

c

QUADRUPLE GRID

d

FIGURE 134

than a number of separate simple beams due to the fact that load sharing between the beams of the grid takes place, as a result of the interconnection.

The more lightly loaded beams help the more heavily loaded ones, thus providing for a more uniformly loaded and efficient structure. The structural depth can be reduced.

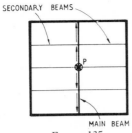

FIGURE 135

The load in a grid structure also flows towards all the supports as shown by the arrows for the rectangular grid in Fig. 134a. This contrasts with a similar simple system of a primary and secondary beams, as shown in Fig. 135, where the main beam has to carry all the secondary beams with the load therefore flowing towards only two supports. In a grid structure therefore, the columns are also more uniformly loaded.

The fabrication of the grid becomes more expensive however due to the connections at the points of intersection. In steel the joints can be welded. In concrete, the beams can be poured in place and so the monolithic joints present no difficulty.

Grids can be of various types. If the beams run at right angles to one another, the grid is called a **rectangular grid** and is shown in Fig. 134a. When the area to be covered (as floor or roof) becomes a deep rectangle with one side much longer than the other, the rectangular grid becomes inefficient because the shorter beams carry a greater share of the load. It is then more efficient to use a **skew grid** as shown in Fig. 134b. This makes the beams of more equal length even over rectangular areas. **Triangular grids** have three sets of members as shown in Fig. 134c and the **quadruple grid** has four sets of members as shown in Fig. 134d. In these latter types, the joints become even more complex because of the number of members and the angles involved.

9.2 The analysis of grids

The simplest type of grid structure consists of two beams interconnected at their centers and such an elementary grid system has already been briefly considered in the discussion on complex load paths in 3.1 and has been shown in Fig. 18. Consider the same grid structure shown diagrammatically in Fig. 136. The equation of compatibility then requires that since the beams are interconnected at **O**, the deflection of the beam **AB** should be equal to the deflection of the beam **CD** at **O**. The load **W** therefore splits into two com-

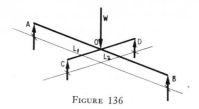

FIGURE 136

ponents W_1 and W_2 so that the beams deflect by the same amount. This is how load sharing takes place, because the stiffer beam takes more load to have the same deflection as the weaker beam which takes less load. If the load on the beam **AB** is W_1 the deflection of the beam at the center is,

$$\delta_1 = \frac{W_1 L_1{}^3}{48EI_1}$$

If the load on the beam **CD** is W_2 its deflection at the center can be got as,

$$\delta_2 = \frac{W_2 L_2{}^3}{48EI_2}$$

Since the deflection of the two beams at **O** must be the same we have,

$$\frac{W_1 L_1{}^3}{48EI_1} = \frac{W_2 L_2{}^3}{48EI_2}$$

Also $W_1 + W_2 = W$. From the above relationship, the value of W_1 and W_2 can be obtained as,

$$W_1 = \frac{W}{1 + \left(\dfrac{L_1}{L_2}\right)^3 \left(\dfrac{I_2}{I_1}\right)}$$

.... 49

$$W_2 = \frac{W}{1 + \left(\dfrac{L_2}{L_1}\right)^3 \left(\dfrac{I_1}{I_2}\right)}$$

The Eqns. 49 bring out a feature of analysis and design which needs some explanation. The values of I_1 and I_2 are quantities which can be exactly determined only after the design of the beams has been actually carried out and the sizes obtained. But the analysis which comes before the design is dependent on these values. It follows that the values of I_1 and I_2, or at least the ratio of $\dfrac{I_1}{I_2}$, have to be approximately estimated for the purposes of analysis. After the design has been completed and the sections have been chosen, the values of I_1 and I_2 (or their ratio) can be exactly determined and it is then necessary to check that the assumption made in the analysis was reasonably correct. If not, the analysis and hence the design may have to be reviewed. A realistic assumption is to have all the beams of the same section. This leads to a uniform structural depth which for a grid may be architecturally very pleasing. Under this assumption, $I_1 = I_2$ and Eqns. 49 reduce to,

$$W_1 = \frac{W}{1 + \left(\dfrac{L_1}{L_2}\right)^3}$$

$$W_2 = \frac{W}{1 + \left(\dfrac{L_2}{L_1}\right)^3}$$

50

With W_1 and W_2 now determined, the bending moments can now be calculated. The approach to the analysis of larger grids is the same, but the method needs to be more systematic in its application since the structure is several times statically indeterminate, depending on the number of points of interconnection, leading to a set of simultaneous equations. A grid structure of any sizable proportions can therefore only be solved by the help of the computer and this aspect of the problem will be considered in Chapter 12. The load propagation through a grid structure will be better appreciated however by a simple example taken here.

Example 9.2.1

Analyse the simple rectangular grid structure shown in Fig. 137. Draw the bending moment and shear force diagram for each beam.

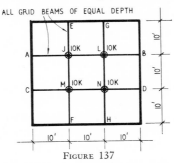

FIGURE 137

For purposes of an understanding of the method of analysis, the grid can be looked upon as two sets of beams **AB, CD** and **EF, GH**. Any one set may be assumed to run above the other set, separated by a small distance and connected by short vertical compressive links at the points of interconnection **J, L, M** and **N** as shown in Fig. 138. The assumption here made is that the

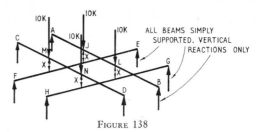

FIGURE 138

set of beams **AB** and **CD** run at the top and take all the vertical 10 K loads on the structure. The short vertical links are assumed to transfer only a vertical force **X** between the sets of beams thus providing for load sharing between the sets of beams. This is purely an imaginary picture since the beams all run at the same level and short vertical links do not exist, but it structurally represents the same system if the effect of torsion in grids (briefly discussed in 3.5 and shown in Fig. 24) is neglected. Naturally any set can be assumed at top or bottom without affecting the final answer in any way.

These short vertical links can now be cut, if the forces **X** are left in place and taken into account, since all that the vertical links do is to transfer the vertical forces from one set of beams to the other. The structure has now been reduced to four individual beams with external loads and forces **X** acting on them as shown in Fig. 139. As the beams are interconnected it

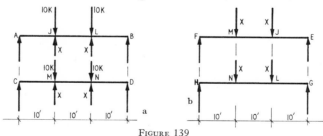

FIGURE 139

follows that the deflection of any two beams at a point of interconnection must be the same. This establishes compatibility of the four beams in the grid structure. The equations of compatibility are therefore,

$$\delta J_{AB} = \delta J_{EF}, \ \delta L_{AB} = \delta L_{GH}, \ \delta M_{CD} = \delta M_{EF}, \ \delta N_{CD} = \delta N_{GH} \ \text{...........} \ 51$$

In this particular case, the structure is perfectly symmetrical and the loading is perfectly symmetrical as well with the result that all the link forces are the same and equal to **X**. If the loading were to be perfectly general, the link forces would be X_1, X_2, X_3 and X_4. The four equations of compatibility would then lead to four simultaneous equations, the solution of which would determine the unknown link forces X_1, X_2, X_3 and X_4.

For the example taken, consider any one of the equations of compatibility say $\delta J_{AB} = \delta J_{EF}$ then,

$$\delta J_{AB} = -\mathbf{X} \times \frac{8}{486}\frac{\mathbf{L}^3}{\mathbf{EI}} - \mathbf{X} \times \frac{7}{486}\frac{\mathbf{L}^3}{\mathbf{EI}} + 10 \times \frac{8}{486}\frac{\mathbf{L}^3}{\mathbf{EI}}$$

$$+ 10 \times \frac{7}{486}\frac{\mathbf{L}^3}{\mathbf{EI}} \quad\text{---} \quad 52$$

The sign convention, chosen arbitrarily, is that downward deflections are positive and upward deflections are negative. Each term of Eqn. 52 is the deflection at $\mathbf{J}$ in the beam $\mathbf{AB}$ under each load acting alone. The four terms together therefore, give the total deflection at $\mathbf{J}$ in the beam $\mathbf{AB}$ under all the loads acting together. It should be noted here that the deflection at $\mathbf{J}$ when a load is applied at $\mathbf{J}$ is $\dfrac{8}{486}\dfrac{\mathbf{L}^3}{\mathbf{EI}}$ for a unit load of 1 K. The deflection at $\mathbf{J}$ when the load is applied at $\mathbf{L}$ is only $\dfrac{7}{486}\dfrac{\mathbf{L}^3}{\mathbf{EI}}$ however for a unit load of 1 K.

The deflection at $\mathbf{J}$ in the beam $\mathbf{EF}$ under its loading can be similarly got as,

$$\delta J_{EF} = +\mathbf{X} \times \frac{8}{486}\frac{\mathbf{L}^3}{\mathbf{EI}} + \mathbf{X} \times \frac{7}{486}\frac{\mathbf{L}^3}{\mathbf{EI}} \quad\text{---} \quad 53$$

Since the beams $\mathbf{AB}$ and $\mathbf{EF}$ are of the same material, have the same length $\mathbf{L} = 30$ ft, and are assumed to have the same cross section and hence the same second moment of area $\mathbf{I}$, the deflections at $\mathbf{J}$ can be simplified by deleting $\dfrac{\mathbf{L}^3}{486\mathbf{EI}}$ from all the terms. The deflections of the two beams at $\mathbf{J}$

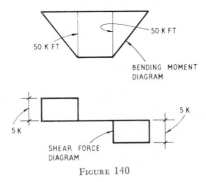

50 K FT

50 K FT

BENDING MOMENT
DIAGRAM

5 K

5 K

SHEAR FORCE
DIAGRAM

FIGURE 140

can now be equated and we have,

$$-15\,\mathbf{X} + 150 = +15\,\mathbf{X}$$

$$30\,\mathbf{X} = 150$$

$$\mathbf{X} = +5\,\mathrm{K}$$

The positive sign to the value of **X** confirms that the direction chosen for the link force (in this case compressive) was correct. The grid structure has now been analysed and the bending moment and shear force diagrams for each beam can be individually drawn. In this example, the bending moment and shear force diagrams for all the beams are identical and are shown in Fig. 140.

9.3 Plates

A flat structure that is not made of discrete members but consists of a continuous surface such as a concrete floor or roof slab, plywood sheathing, etc, is termed as a plate structure. Such structures are very useful in building construction since they not only carry the structural loads but provide the surface for enclosure at the same time as well. They do not therefore need a separate system to enclose the space. The finishing can be applied directly to the structure itself.

In order to understand plate behavior it is essential to understand two important concepts. The first is that of continuity itself. Consider a series of discrete strips as shown in Fig. 141 and loaded with a line load at **EF** on the strip **ACBD**. Under this loading, the strip deflects, leaving adjoining strips undeflected and unstressed. If the strips were connected together to form a plate surface, the deflection of the strip **ACBD** could not occur without the deflection of the adjoining strips occurring as well. The deflection of the adjoining strips would have to be the same, for continuity to be maintained, along the boundaries **AC** and **BD**, as the deflection of the loaded strip itself. In effect the adjoining strip **ACHG** gives some support to the loaded strip along the boundary **AC** and carries some of the load which is transferred to it along the boundary **AC**. The same applies to the adjoining strip **BDKL** along the boundary **BD**.

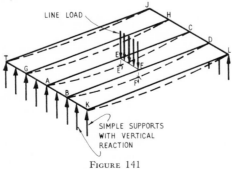

FIGURE 141

As the load is applied to the adjoining strip along the edge **AC**, the strip will twist as it deflects. It cannot however deform without deforming its adjoining strip **GHJT** along the boundary **GH**. It can be seen therefore that at the same time that the load is being propagated towards the supports of the loaded strip, **AB** and **CD**, it is also being partially propagated sideways (or laterally) to adjoining strips so that the final deflection of the plate is a continuous one in both directions. If the plate shown in Fig. 141 were to have a support along the boundary edges **TJ** and **KL**, the strips could be considered as running in both directions. The load is therefore shared by all elements of the plate and this leads to a more efficient structural system.

The second important concept is the **Poisson's** effect. Consider the strip acted upon by a tension in the longitudinal direction as shown in Fig. 142. As the material stretches in the longitudinal direction, it causes an elastic shortening in the lateral direction as shown in Fig. 142. In effect a lateral strain is set up and this is the Poisson's effect. The Poisson's ratio v is then defined as,

$$v = \frac{\text{lateral strain}}{\text{longitudinal strain}} \dotfill 54$$

In a single strip as shown in Fig. 142, or in a discrete member, this strain merely causes an infinitesimally small change in dimension and can very appropriately be neglected. In a plate however, these lateral strains and hence deformations cannot freely occur with the result that stresses and moments are set up in the lateral direction.

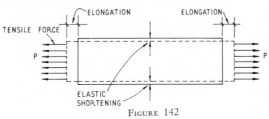

FIGURE 142

Plate action is very useful in structural design since it is efficient in transferring load in all directions from the points of application. The efficiency of such transfer however depends also on the **aspect ratio** of the sides which is the ratio of the length of the sides. Consider the **one way slab** shown in Fig. 143a, uniformly loaded over its entire area. In this slab, most of the load flows along the shorter span only, because the slab is long and narrow. The result is a one way action which is not very different from the action of a series of beams in the shorter direction. Since all the strips are loaded they are all deflecting the same amount and so there is no real sharing of the load in the lateral direction. One way slabs or plates are therefore not classified as true plates. They are analysed and designed by considering a

1 ft representative strip of the slab and treating it as a beam 1 ft wide. This is shown in Fig. 143a. In a reinforced concrete one way slab the main steel hence runs in the shorter direction with only secondary, or temperature and shrinkage, steel in the longer direction. If the slab is square or almost so, with an aspect ratio less than 2, the load flows in both directions towards the supports and plate action does take place. Such a slab is called a **two way slab**, shown in Fig. 143b.

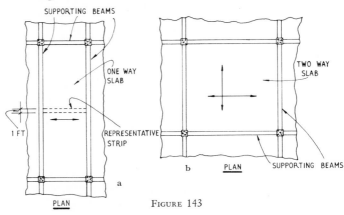

FIGURE 143

A theoretical analysis of plate action shows that the plate or slab may be considered as one way if the aspect ratio of the sides $\left(\dfrac{a}{b}\right)$ is greater than or equal to 2 $\left(\dfrac{a}{b} \geqq 2\right)$ and as two way if the aspect ratio is less than 2 $\left(\dfrac{a}{b} < 2\right)$.

9.4 Analysis of plates

The actual analysis of plates is very complex. Fortunately a large number of cases of various shapes and types of plates, under a variety of loadings and boundary conditions have been solved and are readily available in any good book on plate theory. All that remains for the Architect is to be able to understand and use the results given. Some typical cases are briefly discussed here.

Consider the two way plate simply supported on all sides as shown in Fig. 144a. The maximum positive moments in the middle of the plate depend on the aspect ratio and are shown for the two directions in Table 9.4.1. As the plate is a continuous surface, the values are all per unit width of plate. A unit width, such as 1 ft has hence to be chosen for design. As the plate is

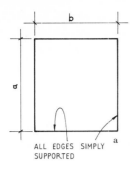

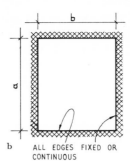

ALL EDGES SIMPLY a   b   ALL EDGES FIXED OR
SUPPORTED   CONTINUOUS

FIGURE 144

simply supported, there are no negative moments. Fig. 144b shows a plate fixed on all sides. The maximum positive moments in the middle of the plate and the maximum negative moments over the supports in both directions are given in Table 9.4.1. Once again, all values are per unit width of plate.

Table 9.4.1
BENDING MOMENTS IN RECTANGULAR PLATES

Aspect ratio $\dfrac{a}{b}$	Simply supported on all four sides	Fixed on all four sides	Corner slabs fixed on two adjacent sides and free on two sides
1.0	$C_a = +0.0479$ $C_b = +0.0479$	$C_a = +0.0231, \ C_a = -0.0513$ $C_b = +0.0231, \ C_b = -0.0513$	$C_a = -0.29$ $C_b = -0.29$
1.3	$C_a = +0.0298$ $C_b = +0.0694$	$C_a = +0.0131, \ C_a = -0.0333$ $C_b = +0.0327, \ C_b = -0.0687$	$C_a = -0.35$ $C_b = -0.35$
1.5	$C_a = +0.0221$ $C_b = +0.0812$	$C_a = +0.0090, \ C_a = -0.0253$ $C_b = +0.0368, \ C_b = -0.0757$	$C_a = -0.37$ $C_b = -0.37$
2.0	$C_a = +0.0116$ $C_b = +0.1017$	$C_a = +0.0039, \ C_a = -0.0143$ $C_b = +0.0412, \ C_b = -0.0829$	$C_a = -0.43$ $C_b = -0.43$

Note: In all cases,

$$M_a = C_a w a^2$$

$$M_b = C_b w b^2$$

A corner balcony slab is shown in Fig. 145 and the maximum negative moments, per unit width of slab, are shown in Table 9.4.1. These maximum moments occur at the roots **A** and **B** as shown in Fig. 145. The positive moments are almost zero in such a cantilevered type of slab.

The values for various types of plates and under various types of loads are

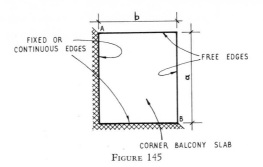

FIGURE 145

theoretical values which have been calculated for plates with $\nu = 0.3$, irrespective of the material. They can be used for slabs in reinforced concrete or plywood sheathing and are approximately correct even though the Poisson's ratio may vary. But all these cases have been calculated for single plates and the Architect needs therefore to reduce his case down to a standard case to be able to abstract the values that he will then use for design.

Consider the floor arrangement shown in Fig. 146. The slab **A** is a corner balcony slab. The slab is continuous over the secondary and the main beam but is not fully fixed. The values given in Table 9.4.1 are for a corner balcony slab that is fixed along the two edges. The Architect can therefore make the reasonable assumption that continuity, since it generates negative moments over the support edges, is equivalent to fixity along that edge. He may then use the values for corner balcony slabs given in Table 9.4.1 and design his slab **A**. The slab shown in Fig. 143b is continuous over all four supporting beams, but may be assumed to be fixed along all four edges and the values

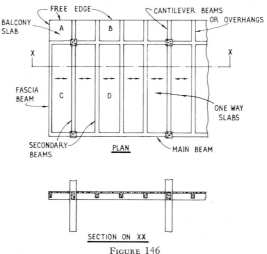

FIGURE 146

then given in Table 9.4.1, for a plate fixed on all four sides, may be used in design.

The slabs **C** and **D** shown in Fig. 146 are one way slabs and present no difficulty in the analysis. They may be analysed by considering a 1 ft representative strip that runs continuous over several secondary beams and is simply supported on the end fascia beam. The fascia beam is itself simply supported on the tips of the main beams which are cantilevered over the columns. For the design of slabs **C** and **D** therefore, the concrete coefficients given in Table 7.3.1 should be used. The slab **B** shown in Fig. 146 is continuous over three edges and free on the fourth. The equivalent plate case would therefore be a plate that was fixed on three sides and free on the fourth.

The design of slabs in reinforced concrete is also governed by the concrete Code as laid down in ACI 318-71 and will therefore be considered in greater detail in 9.5. A simple example of a plate in plywood will be considered here.

Example 9.4.1

Determine the maximum bending moments in a square plywood plate 4 ft × 4 ft loaded with a total load of 100 lbs/sq ft for the following boundary conditions:

a. When all the four edges are simply supported,
b. When all the four edges are continuous over the supports,
c. When two adjacent edges are continuous over the supports and the other two are free.

a. For the plywood plate,

$$\mathbf{a} = 4 \text{ ft}$$

$$\mathbf{b} = 4 \text{ ft}$$

$$\mathbf{w} = 100 \text{ lbs/sq ft}$$

$$\frac{\mathbf{a}}{\mathbf{b}} = 1$$

Referring to Table 9.4.1 when all edges are simply supported and $\dfrac{\mathbf{a}}{\mathbf{b}} = 1$

we have,

$$\mathbf{M_a} = + \mathbf{C_a \, w \, a^2} = + 0.0479 \times 100 \times 4^2 = + 76.6 \text{ lb ft/ft}$$

$$\mathbf{M_b} = + \mathbf{C_b \, w \, b^2} = + 0.0479 \times 100 \times 4^2 = + 76.6 \text{ lb ft/ft}$$

b. Since all the edges are continuous over the supports it may be assumed that all edges are fixed. Referring to Table 9.4.1, when all edges are fixed and

$\dfrac{a}{b} = 1$ we have,

M_a at the center of the plate $= + C_a \, w \, a^2 = + 0.0231 \times 100 \times 4^2 =$
$\phantom{M_a \text{ at the center of the plate} = + C_a w a^2 = +} 37.0$ lb ft/ft

M_b at the center of the plate $= + C_b \, w \, b^2 = + 0.0231 \times 100 \times 4^2 =$
$\phantom{M_b \text{ at the center of the plate} = + C_b w b^2 = +} 37.0$ lb ft/ft

M_a over the support $= - C_a \, w \, a^2 = - 0.0513 \times 100 \times 4^2 = - 82.1$ lb ft/ft

M_b over the support $= - C_b \, w \, b^2 = - 0.0513 \times 100 \times 4^2 = - 82.1$ lb ft/ft

c. These support conditions cause the plate to cantilever from the adjacent sides which may be assumed as fixed. Referring to Table 9.4.1 for the corner balcony slab, for $\dfrac{a}{b} = 1$ we have,

M_a over the root of the support edge $= - C_a \, w \, b^2 = - 0.29 \times 100 \times 4^2$
$\phantom{M_a \text{ over the root of the support edge} = - C_a w b^2} = - 464.0$ lb ft/ft

M_b over the root of the support edge $= - C_b \, w \, b^2 = - 0.29 \times 100 \times 4^2$
$\phantom{M_b \text{ over the root of the support edge} = - C_b w b^2} = - 464.0$ lb ft/ft

In all of the above cases, the moments are per 1 ft width of the plate in a direction at right angles to the direction of the moment. The plywood plate can now be designed for the maximum moments in each case. The above example shows very clearly how important the boundary conditions are and how drastically the maximum design moments can be affected by them.

9.5 Reinforced concrete slabs

Reinforced concrete slabs, so commonly used in floor and roof construction, can be of several types. The one way slab has already been considered in the discussion on plates in 9.3 and 9.4. Two way slabs can be of various types. If the slab is supported on or continuous over edge beams, as shown in Fig. 143b, the slab thickness is small leading to a very economical structure. The old Code ACI 318-63 required that the thickness of the slab be at least $\dfrac{1}{180}$ of the perimeter of the slab. In more meaningful terms, a slab 20 ft $\times$ 20 ft supported by edge beams and under normal floor loading was about 5½ in. to 6 in. thick. The slab transfers its load to the edge beams which are considerably deeper. The disadvantage of such an arrangement is that the headroom under the beams is less than the headroom beneath the slab. The beams form large panels and in some cases can interfere with the ducting.

If deep edge beams are objectionable, the **flat slab** shown in Fig. 147 can

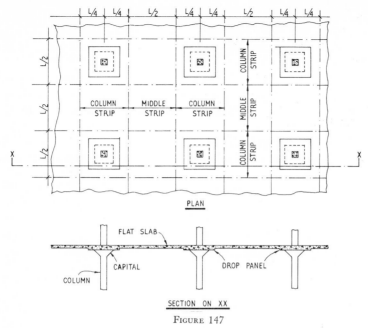

PLAN

FLAT SLAB

CAPITAL   DROP PANEL

COLUMN

SECTION ON XX

FIGURE 147

be very useful. In the flat slab, the edge beams are eliminated. This has the advantage of increasing the headroom through the structure. It has the disadvantage that the slab needs to be thicker and so is more uneconomical at least in material cost. The worst stresses in a flat slab occur over the columns since at these points the load is transferred into the columns. The thickness of the slab can therefore be increased over the columns by the provision of **drop panels** as shown in Fig. 147. Furthermore the column can also have a **capital** if necessary.

If the bays are large and the thickness of the flat slab is likely to be excessive, a **waffle slab** may be used as shown in Fig. 148. A waffle slab consists of a thin top slab cast integrally with solid ribs running in both directions forming small square panels or waffles when looked at from underneath. The formwork for such a slab consists of steel or reinforced polyester (FRP) square **domes** or **pans**. The slabs are hence also sometimes referred to as

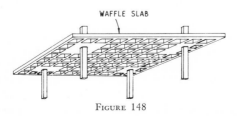

WAFFLE SLAB

FIGURE 148

dome slabs. The overall structural depth of this type of construction is a little more than in flat slab construction. As in the flat slab, the slab can be made stronger over the columns by filling in some of the panels or waffles, as shown in Fig. 148.

The analysis and design of all these types of slabs is not very easy. The design requires a detailed study of the concrete Code ACI 318-71. This study can be helped by **Notes on ACI 318-71, Building Code Requirements with Design Applications** published by the Portland Cement Association (PCA). The Code ACI 318-71 now outdates ACI 318-63 and will itself be outdated by the next ACI Code which will be based on further experience and testing. Whilst fundamental structural principles, outlined in this book, do not change, the Codes undoubtedly will. Nevertheless a study of the Codes is valuable to the Architect for the design of reinforced concrete structures.

The first basic information given by the Code, which helps the Architect form some ideas on the thickness of the concrete slab that he is likely to need, is the requirement of minimum thickness as specified by the Code. A two way concrete slab supported on edge beams cannot be less than $3\frac{1}{2}$ in. thick. For flat slabs without beams but with drop panels extending at least $\frac{1}{6}$ span, the thickness of the slab cannot be less than 4 in. For flat slabs without drop panels, the thickness of the slab cannot be less than 5 in. These are the absolute minimum values and for small spans and light loading will in fact be the governing thicknesses. For other spans, the thicknesses may be more than the minimum specified. For flat slabs, the thickness may be approximately determined as,

$$h = \frac{L_n}{33} \quad\quad\quad 55$$

where **h** is the thickness of the slab and L_n is the clear span in the long direction.

The Architect thus has now some idea of the thickness of his slab as also the loads on his beams and columns and can design them without difficulty. If a more detailed investigation is to be carried out, it is necessary to refer to the Code ACI 318-71 under **Slab Systems with Multiple Square or Rectangular Panels.** All slabs considered previously, except one way slabs, come under this classification. The analysis and design of a flat slab will be briefly examined.

The flat slab has been shown in Fig. 147. If the span between the columns is **L** in any direction, the slab may be assumed to consist of column strips and middle strips. A column strip is the strip on either side of the column 0.25L wide with a total width of 0.50L as in Fig. 147. If the spans are unequal, **L** is the shorter span. The middle strip is the strip between adjacent column strips. This applies to both directions as shown in Fig. 147.

The total static design moment M_o in any span in one direction is given by,

$$M_o = \frac{w\,L_2\,L_n^2}{8} \quad\text{..} \quad 56$$

where,

  $w =$ loading in lbs/sq ft

  $L_n =$ clear span in the direction being considered,

  $L_2 =$ panel width in the direction at right angles to the direction being considered.

The **total moment** M_o is now split into the negative and positive design moments. For interior bays such as in Fig. 147, the percentages are as follows:

Negative design moment $= 65\%$ of $M_o = 0.65\,M_o$

Positive design moment $= 35\%$ of $M_o = 0.35\,M_o$ 57

The sum of the negative and positive design moments must equal M_o. Each of these moments has now to be split into two parts, one part of which is taken by the column strip and the remainder taken by the middle strip. For an interior panel of a flat slab without edge beams, the values are as follows:

  Negative design moment in the column strip $=$
    $0.75 \times$ Negative design moment

  Negative design moment in the middle strip $=$
    $0.25 \times$ Negative design moment

  Positive design moment in the column strip $=$
    $0.60 \times$ Positive design moment

  Positive design moment in the middle strip $=$
    $0.40 \times$ Positive design moment

The design of the slab for these moments can be easily carried out. The total load being transferred into any column has then to be calculated and estimating the size of the column, the punching shear stress should be checked to ensure that the column does not punch through the slab or the drop panel. The analysis will be made clear by an example taken here, but it ought to be emphasized strongly that the analysis that has been considered is a very small part that has been covered in the Code ACI 318-71 and has been considerably simplified. The Code covers a number of different types of multiple square or rectangular slabs, with and without edge beams, stipulates the limitations or conditions under which the analysis is valid and presents other modifications which have not been discussed here. For an accurate and complete interpretation of the Code, in all cases the Architect is referred to the Code itself.

Example 9.5.1

Determine the design moments in the flat slab of an interior bay of a floor of a multi-storey high rise building for the following data:

Span $\mathbf{L} = 20$ ft in both directions

Loading $= 100$ lbs/sq ft dead load $+ 80$ lbs/sq ft live load

Column size $= 18$ in. $\times$ 18 in. assumed at that floor level

Both of the directions are identical in this case. Consider any one direction. Then for that direction,

$$\mathbf{L_n} = 20 - 1.5 = 18.5 \text{ ft}$$

$$\mathbf{L_2} = 20 \text{ ft}$$

The ultimate load $\mathbf{w}$ for purposes of design is,

$$\mathbf{w} = 1.4 \, \mathbf{D.L.} + 1.7 \, \mathbf{L.L.}$$

$$= 1.4 \times 100 + 1.7 \times 80 = 140 + 136 = 276 \text{ lbs/sq ft}$$

Using Eqn. 56 we have,

$$\mathbf{M_o} = \frac{\mathbf{w} \, \mathbf{L_2} \, \mathbf{L_n}^2}{8} = \frac{276 \times 20 \times 18.5^2}{8} = 236153 \text{ lb ft per panel}$$

It should be noted here, that the moment is the **total** design moment (positive $+$ negative) on the entire width of the panel. The moment can now be split into positive and negative by use of Eqn. 57 which gives,

Negative design moment $= 0.65 \, \mathbf{M_o} = 0.65 \times 236153 = -153499$ lb ft

Positive design moment $= 0.35 \, \mathbf{M_o} = 0.35 \times 236153 = +82654$ lb ft

Each of these moments can now be split into column strip and middle strip moments and we have,

Negative design moment in the column strip $=$
0.75 $\times$ ($-$ 153499) $= -$ 115124 lb ft

Negative design moment in the middle strip $=$
0.25 $\times$ ($-$ 153499) $= -$ 38375 lb ft

Positive design moment in the column strip $=$
0.60 $\times$ ($+$ 82654) $= +$ 49592 lb ft

Positive design moment in the middle strip =
0.40 × (+ 82654) = + 33062 lb ft

If a drop panel is provided, it has to be designed for the ultimate maximum negative moment of − 115124 lb ft on a 10 ft width. The slab itself has then to be designed for the ultimate maximum positive moment of + 49592 lb ft on a width of 10 ft. The punching shear stress on the perimeter of the column should be checked after the slab has been designed for the moments and its thickness has been determined.

9.6 Plates or slabs of various shapes

In his Architectural design, the Architect may desire to provide slabs which are not necessarily rectangular. They may be circular, polygonal or even triangular. The concrete Code ACI 318-71 does not deal explicitly with concrete slabs of these shapes. The design of such slabs is approximate and in certain cases very simple. Plate theory has to be used. The analysis as before requires the determination of the design moments and design can then be carried out as discussed in 5.10.

Consider the circular plate or slab shown in Fig. 149, fixed or continuous over the boundary edge. The maximum positive and negative design moments under uniformly distributed loading are given in Table 9.6.1. This table also gives the positive design moments in the radial and tangential directions when the slab is simply supported on the boundary. In this case, the negative moments are zero.

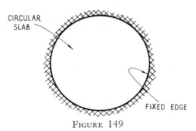

FIGURE 149

Table 9.6.1
BENDING MOMENTS IN CIRCULAR PLATES

Simply supported circular plate	$M_r = + 0.051\,\mathbf{w}\mathbf{D}^2$ at center
Fixed circular plate	$M_r = + 0.016\,\mathbf{w}\mathbf{D}^2$ at center
	$M_r = - 0.031\,\mathbf{w}\mathbf{D}^2$ at boundary

Example 9.6.1

A circular slab over a conference room is fixed along its boundary edge as in Fig. 149. If the diameter of the slab is 20 ft and the total loading is 200 lbs/sq ft, determine the design moments in the slab.

Assume that the dead load is 100 lbs/sq ft and the live load is 100 lbs/sq ft. $D = 20$ ft.

$$w = 1.4\,\textbf{D.L.} + 1.7\,\textbf{L.L.}$$

$$w = 1.4 \times 100 + 1.7 \times 100 = 140 + 170 = 310 \text{ lbs/sq ft}$$

From Table 9.6.1 for a circular slab fixed along its boundary edge we have,

M_r **maximum at the boundary** $= -0.031\,w\,D^2 = -0.031 \times 310 \times 20^2 =$
$$-3844 \text{ lb ft/ft}$$

M_r **maximum at the center** $= +0.016\,w\,D^2 = +0.016 \times 310 \times 20^2 =$
$$+1984 \text{ lb ft/ft}$$

The slab would be designed for the maximum negative moment of -3844 lb ft/ft. The thickness would then be kept uniform but the reinforcement at the center would be reduced because the maximum positive moment at the center is less. The reinforcement at the boundary would be at the top of the slab, whereas at the center it would be at the bottom. The main steel would be placed radially whilst the secondary steel would be placed tangentially.

The maximum shear force is the total load on the perimeter of the slab. This can therefore be determined as,

$$V = \frac{w\,\dfrac{\pi D^2}{4}}{\pi D} = \frac{w\,D}{4} = \frac{310 \times 20}{4} = 1550 \text{ lbs/ft}$$

As has also been seen before, the shear force in slabs is usually small and not critical to the design of the slab.

Polygonal slabs are generally of regular polygons. A hexagonal slab is shown in Fig. 150a. The exact mathematical analysis of a polygonal plate is very complex. It has been determined however, that the maximum bending moments and shear forces are approximately equal to those obtained by

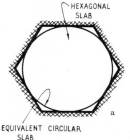

HEXAGONAL SLAB

TRIANGULAR SLAB

EQUIVALENT CIRCULAR SLAB

EQUIVALENT CIRCULAR SLAB

a

b

FIGURE 150

the analysis of an equivalent inscribed circular plate as shown in Fig. 150a. The same approach also applies with reasonable accuracy to triangular plates or slabs. The equivalent inscribed circular slab roughly defines the behavior of the triangular slab as shown in Fig. 150b. The answers that result from such approximations can at times be seriously in error, but in the end to the Architect, approximate answers are infinitely better than no answers at all.

It should be noted that the boundary conditions of the actual polygonal or triangular plate or slab, apply as well to the equivalent circular plate or slab, considered for purposes of analysis.

Example 9.6.2

For the square plywood plate considered in Example 9.4.1 determine the maximum moments that would have been obtained with an equivalent inscribed circular plate. For the plate $a = 4$ ft, $b = 4$ ft, $w = 100$ lbs/sq ft.

a. All four edges of the plate are simply supported. The diameter of the equivalent inscribed circular plate $D = 4$ ft. The maximum positive bending moment at the center of a simply supported circular plate can be obtained from Table 9.6.1. as,

$$\mathbf{M_r} \text{ maximum at the center} = + 0.051 \text{ } \mathbf{w} \text{ } \mathbf{D}^2 = + 0.051 \times 100 \times 4^2 =$$
$$81.6 \text{ lb ft/ft}$$

b. The four edges of the plate are continuous over the supports and are assumed as fixed. The maximum positive and negative moments for the inscribed circular plate with fixed boundary can be obtained from Table 9.6.1 as,

$$\mathbf{M_r} \text{ maximum at the center} = + 0.016 \text{ } \mathbf{w} \text{ } \mathbf{D}^2 = + 0.016 \times 100 \times 4^2 =$$
$$+ 25.6 \text{ lb ft/ft}$$

$$\mathbf{M_r} \text{ maximum over the support} = - 0.031 \text{ } \mathbf{w} \text{ } \mathbf{D}^2 = - 0.031 \times 100 \times 4^2 =$$
$$- 49.6 \text{ lb ft/ft}$$

A comparison with the values obtained in Example 9.4.1 shows the close relationship, between the exact values as obtained in Example 9.4.1 and the approximate values obtained in this example, for the simply supported case **a**, but much larger discrepancies for the fixed case **b**. The case **c** is not relevant in this example and cannot be considered.

In conclusion it may be stated that the triangular plate and the square plate are rather poor examples for this type of approximation. The results would be much better for other regular polygons with a larger number of sides.

Problems for solution

Example 1: Use the approach followed in Example 9.2.1 to analyse the simple grid shown in Fig. 136. Assume that the load **W** acts only on the beam **AB** at the top. Hence determine the vertical link force **X** between the beams. Both beams are built of the same material and may be assumed to have the same cross section. Neglect the dead load of the beams.

Ans: $X = \dfrac{WL_1^3}{(L_1^3 + L_2^3)}$

Example 2: For the continuous one way slabs shown in Fig. 146, use the concrete coefficients on a 1 ft representative strip to obtain the maximum positive and negative moments in the end span **C**. Span **L** = 10 ft, Loading **w** = 200 lbs/sq ft.

Ans: M positive = + 1818 lb ft/ft, **M** negative = − 2000 lb ft/ft

Example 3: A two way concrete slab on edge beams is shown in Fig. 143b. If the slab is 20 ft × 20 ft and the total load (dead + live) is 200 lbs/sq ft, calculate the maximum positive and negative moments by treating it as a plate.

Ans: Positive moments $M_a = M_b = + 1848$ lb ft/ft

Negative moments $M_a = M_b = - 4104$ lb ft/ft

Example 4: The corner balcony slab **A** in Fig. 146 is 10 ft × 10 ft and has a loading (dead + live) of 200 lbs/sq ft. Calculate the maximum negative moments in the slab by treating it as a plate.

Ans: Negative moments $M_a = M_b = - 5800$ lb ft/ft

Example 5: Use working stress design (**M** $= \dfrac{1}{6}$ **fc bd²**) to calculate the approximate overall depths of all the slabs in Examples 2, 3 and 4 above. Assume #4 bar (½ in. diameter) main steel with ¾ in. clear cover. **fc′** = 4000 psi. Round off your answer to the nearest larger ½ in.

Ans: Example 2, $d_{overall}$ = 4 in.

Example 3, $d_{overall}$ = 5 in.

Example 4, $d_{overall}$ = 5½ in.

Example 6: For the flat slab of Example 9.5.1, determine the overall depth of the drop panel that would be required to ensure that the punching shear stress does not exceed $4\sqrt{fc'}$. Assume #4 bar (½ in. diameter) main slab steel with ¾ in. clear cover. **fc′** = 4000 psi.

Hint: Ultimate shear stress = 253 psi. Total load = 276 × 20 × 20 = 110400 lbs. Perimeter of the column = 18 × 4 = 72 in. ϕ = 0.85.

$$v_c = \frac{V_u}{\phi b d_{eff}}, \; d_{eff} = 7.2 \text{ in.}$$

Ans: $d_{overall} = 8\frac{1}{2}$ in.

Chapter 10
FOLDED PLATE STRUCTURES

10.1 The folded plate

The structural behavior of the flat plate has been seen in 9.3. Such a plate is shown in Fig. 151a. It can be seen that the structural depth of the plate is its thickness **t** and that this thickness is very small in comparison to its overall dimensions. Since it is this thickness that is the important structural dimension for resisting the load which acts normal to the plate surface, the span over which the plate can carry the load is necessarily limited. If the spans are large or the loads are heavy, the thickness of the plate or slab becomes very large and hence uneconomical in terms of the materials cost.

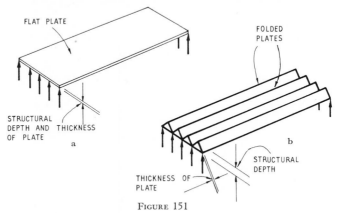

FIGURE 151

A more efficient way to span large spans with a small thickness of plate is to fold the plate as shown in Fig. 151b. Such a folded plate now has a structural depth which is much larger than its actual thickness as shown in Fig. 151b. Folded plate behavior can also be understood in another way. The action of the fold is to resolve the vertical loading into components which act in the planes of the plates as shown in Fig. 152. The plane of the plate again has a much larger structural depth as an inclined beam than the thickness of the plate. The transverse component has still to be taken by

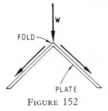

FIGURE 152

the thickness **t** but the span of the plate is now only the plate width between the folds and is quite small. The folded plates are supported on rigid end diaphragms as shown in Fig. 153. The folded plates then transfer the load

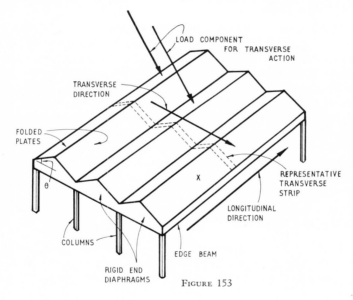

FIGURE 153

as beams into these rigid end diaphragms which are supported on columns. These rigid end diaphragms can either be thin, solid vertical plates as shown in Fig. 153 or ridged end beams as shown in Fig. 154. In the latter case a tie member may be used to tie the tops of the columns together as shown in Fig. 154.

10.2 Types of folded plate structures

Folded plate structures are primarily of two types—**prismatic** and **non-prismatic.** Prismatic folded plate structures use rectangular plates and are

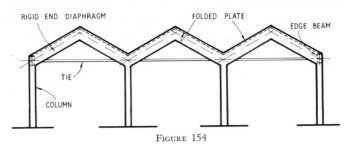

FIGURE 154

shown in Fig. 155. The **Vee type** folded plate roof structure, with each unit having two plates, is shown in Fig. 155a. Fig. 155b shows a prismatic folded plate roof structure with a larger number of plates.

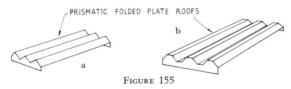

FIGURE 155

Non-prismatic folded plate structures can be of three types—**pyramidal, prismoidal** and **composite.** Pyramidal structures, such as pavilion or church roofs, are a rather special case of folded plate structures. They can be based on any regular polygon. A pyramidal folded plate roof structure based on the rectangle is shown in Fig. 156. Such structures can range from the **tetrahedron,** based on the triangle at one end of the scale, to the **cone** based on the circle, at the other. The cone in fact represents a pyramidal structure based on a regular polygon with an infinite number of sides. The disadvantage of pyramidal structures is that if used as single roofs, the plate spans become very large and the transverse component of the load may require a large thickness of plate.

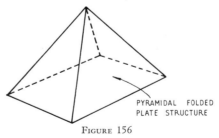

FIGURE 156

Prismoidal folded plate structures are an intermediate form between prismatic and single pyramidal structures. A prismoidal structure can be looked upon either as the frustrum of a pyramid (obtained by cutting off the apex of the pyramid) or as a prismatic folded plate structure with end plates that are not vertical but inclined (or hipped). Such a prismoidal folded plate structure is shown in Fig. 157.

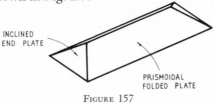

FIGURE 157

The most interesting folded plate structures are composite folded plate structures. The distinguishing feature of such structures is that if the structure is considered as a whole, it is folded not only laterally but longitudinally as well. Some examples of composite folded plate structures are shown in Fig. 158. A three pin, pitched roof, folded plate portal frame is shown in

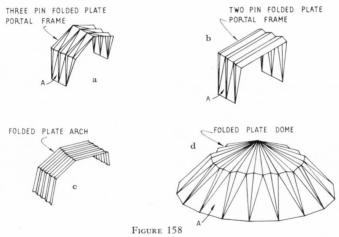

FIGURE 158

Fig. 158a whilst Fig. 158b shows a two pin, rectangular folded plate portal frame. A composite folded plate arch is shown in Fig. 158c and a composite folded plate dome in Fig. 158d. In all of the above structures shown in Fig. 158, the panels marked **A** could be punctured to provide door and window openings. Because of the angles involved, such structures would be very

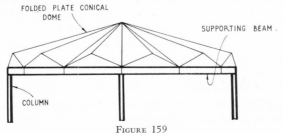

FIGURE 159

suitable in poured in place concrete or light structural plastics sandwich construction and in timber plywood construction—but would be unsuitable in steel. A composite folded plate conical dome is shown in Fig. 159. Another interesting type of folded plate arch structure is shown in Fig. 160a. The entire structure can be built with only one type of unit shown in Fig. 160b. It is hence very suitable for complete prefabrication in precast concrete or structural plastics, where the entire structure can be cast in only one set of forms or in one mold. The unit marked **A** in Fig. 160a is a half longitudinal unit, whereas the unit marked **B** is a quarter unit. For all these units to

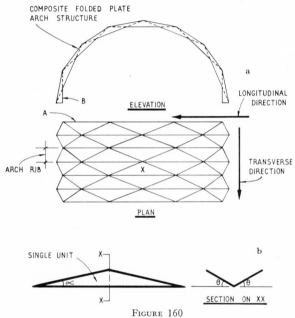

FIGURE 160

mate together to form the structure, the angle between the valley lines of successive units in the same row should be 4α whilst the angle between the valley lines of successive units in adjacent rows should be 2α, where α is the angle of the unit as shown in Fig. 160b. The fold angle θ can vary between practical limits of 15° to 60°. A change in the angle θ alters the stiffness and the total transverse length (but not the span) of the structure. A shallow angle θ leads to a large area being covered by a rather flexible arch structure with shallow folds. A steeper angle θ leads to a smaller area being covered by a stiffer structure with deeper folds.

10.3 Analysis of folded plates

The analysis of folded plate structures, for purposes of design by the Architect, can be split into two parts:

a. The analysis of the plate for transverse plate action under the transverse loading on the plate.

b. The analysis of the structure as a whole for overall longitudinal action.

For transverse plate action consider the prismatic folded plate structure shown in Fig. 153. The rectangular prismatic plates are under the transverse load component of the vertical load as shown in Fig. 153. This transverse load component can be calculated very easily as,

Transverse load component = W Cos θ 58

where,

$$W = \text{vertical load}$$

$$\theta = \text{the fold angle as shown in Fig. 153.}$$

Any of the plates can now be separated out from the structure and analysed for transverse action under this load. The exterior plate, marked **X** in Fig. 153, may be considered to be simply supported on the end diaphragms along the short edges, simply supported on the edge beam and continuous over the fold at the ridge. For transverse action, the fold acts as a positive support which is possible because of the adjoining plate and the angle of the fold. For the prismatic Vee type folded plate structure shown in Fig. 153 however, the transverse plate action can be simplified even still further because the aspect ratio is much greater than 2. It has been seen in 9.3 that if the aspect ratio is greater than 2, the plate is merely a one way plate and can be analysed by considering a representative 1 ft strip in the shorter direction, as shown in Fig. 153. The analysis of the strip can be easily carried out under the transverse component of the vertical load as shown in Fig. 161.

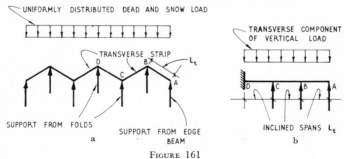

FIGURE 161

Since the transverse strip is absolutely symmetrical and since the loading is symmetrical too, only half of the total spans need to be analysed as shown in Fig. 161b. The transverse strip can be straightened out and assumed as fixed at **D** since the absolute symmetry of the structure does not permit **D** to rotate at all—which is equivalent to a fixed support.

For other complex folded plate structures such as the folded plate arch structure shown in Fig. 160a, the transverse plate action would require the analysis of triangular plates. The transverse component of the vertical load acting normal to the plate is maximum in the unit **X** at the top, as shown in Fig. 160a, and the analysis should be carried out for one of these plates. The plate may be considered as fixed on all sides and may be analysed by substituting the analysis of an inscribed circular plate fixed at its boundary, as discussed in 9.6.

The overall longitudinal action of the structure is easy to appreciate. It is a beam action for the Vee type folded plate structure shown in Fig. 153. For the center two plates, which form a unit, the longitudinal action is shown in Fig. 162. The unit spans as a beam between the rigid end diaphragms. The

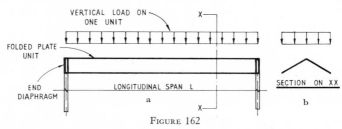

FIGURE 162

load is the total vertical load over one unit. The beam has the cross section as shown in Fig. 162b. For the composite folded plate portal frames of Figs. 158a and b, the overall longitudinal action is the portal frame action. For the composite folded plate arch structures of Figs. 158c and 160, the overall longitudinal action is the arch action. For the composite folded plate domes of Figs. 158d and 159, the overall longitudinal action is the dome action of the structures as a whole.

In some cases, the overall longitudinal action may be a little difficult to determine accurately, but this should not restrict the Architect from understanding his folded plate structure, designing it approximately and providing adequate boundary conditions at the feet or foundations of the structure for the structure to behave in the manner that he has assumed it to behave.

Example 10.3.1

Design a Vee type concrete folded plate prismatic roof structure to cover an area of 36 ft × 50 ft. The snow load is 30 lbs/sq ft.

The Vee type folded plate roof structure shown in Fig. 153 will be designed with the following data:

Chord width of each unit = 12 ft

Span of each unit = 50 ft

Fold angle $\theta = 30°$

Assume that the overall thickness of the plate is 4 in. The loading on the folded plate structure can hence be determined as,

$$\text{Dead load} = 12 \times 4 = 48 \text{ lbs/sq ft}$$
$$\text{Finishing load say} = 12 \text{ lbs/sq ft}$$
$$\text{Total dead load} = 60 \text{ lbs/sq ft}$$
$$\text{Total snow load} = 30 \text{ lbs/sq ft}$$

The self or dead load is per sq ft of inclined surface area whilst the snow load is per sq ft of plan area.

Transverse plate action

The length of each plate is the span of the representative transverse strip and can be calculated as,

$$\mathbf{L_t} = \frac{\textbf{Half the chord width}}{\textbf{Cos } \theta} = \frac{6}{0.8666} = 6.92 \text{ ft}$$

The aspect ratio of the plate is $\frac{50}{6.92} = 7.23$. This is much greater than 2 and so the transverse plate action can be determined by considering a 1 ft representative strip at the center as shown in Fig. 153. The strip runs over the ridges and valleys, which function as supports to the strip. The loading on this transverse strip can be determined as,

$$\text{Snow load} = 30 \times 6 \times 1 = 180 \text{ lbs}$$
$$\text{Dead load} = 60 \times 6.92 \times 1 = 415 \text{ lbs}$$
$$\text{Total load} = 595 \text{ lbs}$$

The load transverse to the plate for transverse action is therefore,

$$\mathbf{W} = 595 \text{ Cos } \theta = 595 \times 0.866 = 515 \text{ lbs}$$

Since the transverse strip is absolutely symmetrical and is loaded absolutely symmetrically, it follows that the slope at the central support $\mathbf{D}$ must be zero. The strip can therefore be analysed for only half the number of spans with a fixed end (zero slope) at $\mathbf{D}$, as shown in Fig. 161b. The analysis can be very easily carried out by the use of the coefficients for continuous concrete beams as given in Table 7.3.1. The maximum moment for purposes of design occurs at the first internal support and is $-\frac{\mathbf{w L_t^2}}{10}$ where $\mathbf{w}$ is the load per ft.

$$\mathbf{BM}_{\max} = -\frac{\mathbf{W L_t}}{10} = -\frac{515 \times 6.92}{10} = 356 \text{ lb ft}$$

Using working stress design and with $fc' = 3000$ psi, the Eqn. 35 gives,

$$\mathbf{M} = \frac{1}{6} \mathbf{fc\ bd^2}$$

where, $\mathbf{fc} = 1350$ psi for $\mathbf{fc'} = 3000$ psi, $\mathbf{b} = 12$ in. and $\mathbf{d} = $ effective depth. We have therefore,

$$356 \times 12 = \frac{1}{6} \times 1350 \times 12 \times \mathbf{d^2}$$

$$\mathbf{d^2} = 1.582$$

$$\mathbf{d} = 1.26 \text{ in.}$$

With such a small effective depth and with both negative and positive moments occurring in different sections of the plate (negative moment at the supports and positive moment at the center) it is realistic to have only one layer of steel or wire mesh reinforcement placed at the center of the plate. The overall depth, which is the thickness of the plate $\mathbf{t}$, can hence be determined as,

$$\mathbf{t} = 2 \times \mathbf{d_{effective}} = 2 \times 1.26 = 2.52 \text{ in. say 3 in.}$$

The steel for transverse action can be assumed to be 1.25% of the concrete area for $\mathbf{fc'} = 3000$ psi and we have,

$$\mathbf{A_s} = 1.25\% \text{ of } \mathbf{bd_{effective}} = \frac{1.25}{100} \times 12 \times 1.26 = 0.189 \text{ sq in./12 in. width}$$

A #3 bar at 6 in. o.c. would give 0.22 sq in./12 in. width, and would be acceptable. The better alternative however is to provide a suitable wire mesh fabric reinforcement for the same area of steel.

Longitudinal beam action for an internal unit

Consider an entire unit with two plates and an inverted Vee cross section as shown in Fig. 162. The beam spans between the rigid end diaphragms. The vertical load on 1 ft length of this unit can be obtained as,

$$\mathbf{w} = 595 \times 2 = 1190 \text{ lbs/ft}$$

The span $\mathbf{L}$ of the beam is 50 ft and the maximum bending moment, as a simply supported beam as calculated in Example 3.7.1 is,

$$\mathbf{BM_{max}} \text{ at center} = \frac{\mathbf{wL^2}}{8} = \frac{1190 \times 50^2}{8} = 372000 \text{ lb ft}$$

The effective vertical depth of the unit is 3.46 ft.

$$\mathbf{d_{effective}} = 3.46 \times 12 = 41.52 \text{ in. say 40 in.}$$

Using working stress design and with $fc = 1350$ psi, Eqn. 35 gives,

$$M = \frac{1}{6} \, fc \, bd^2$$

$$372000 \times 12 = \frac{1}{6} \times 1350 \times b \times 40^2$$

$$b = 12.4 \text{ in.}$$

Since the vertical depth was considered for the beam in the above calculation, the width that has been obtained is the horizontal width as shown in Fig. 163. For the fold angle $\theta = 30°$, $b = 4t$ and therefore,

$$t = 0.25 \times b = 0.25 \times 12.4 = 3.1 \text{ in. say 3 in.}$$

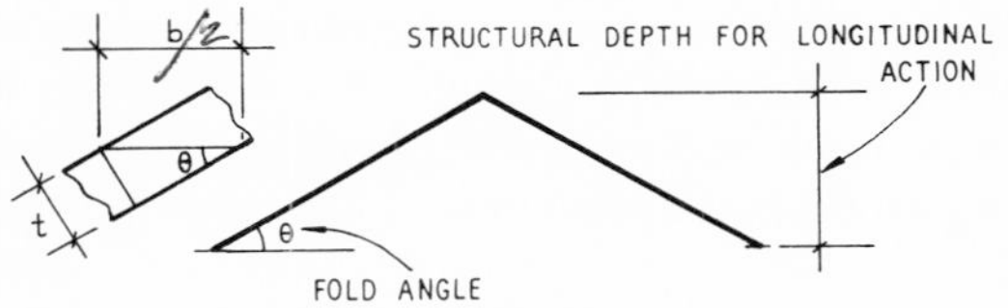

FIGURE 163

Check for shear

A quick check for the shear stress can be carried out very easily. The maximum shear force, as calculated in Example 3.7.1, is,

$$V = \frac{wL}{2} = \frac{1190 \times 50}{2} = 29750 \text{ lbs}$$

The average shearing stress v is therefore,

$$v = \frac{29750}{12 \times 40} = 62 \text{ psi}$$

The permissible shear stress for concrete with $fc' = 3000$ psi as given in Table 4.2.1 is 60 psi. The design is therefore acceptable. It should be remembered that in the loading, the self load was assumed for a 4 in. thickness of plate whereas the actual thickness arrived at is only 3 in.

The area of tension steel A_s for longitudinal action can be determined as 1.25% of the concrete area for $fc' = 3000$ psi.

$$A_s = \frac{1.25}{100} \times 12 \times 40 = 6.0 \text{ sq in.}$$

Use #10 bars, area of each bar $= 1.27$ sq in.

$$\text{Total number of bars required} = \frac{6.0}{1.27} = 4.72 \text{ say 5 nos.}$$

This tension steel for longitudinal action will have to be provided in the valleys and in order to accommodate all the steel, part of the gutter may have to be filled in to provide the concrete cover.

The analysis and design of the composite folded plate arch shown in Fig. 160a has been detailed in the author's other book **Structural Design with Plastics.**

Problems for solution

Example 1: For the Architectural designs arrived at in your Studio courses, examine the possibility of providing and integrating folded plate structures of various types into the designs. Verbalise the load propagation through the structure. Attempt, if possible, an analysis of the transverse and longitudinal actions and determine approximate thicknesses for the plates.

Chapter 11
SHELL STRUCTURES

11.1 Shell surfaces

Curved surfaces have long been known in nature to be very efficient in load transfer. The common egg shell is a simple example of a thin walled doubly curved shell structure which has considerable strength in comparison to the thickness of the wall and its material of construction.

Shell surfaces are efficient because due to curvature, they are capable of propagating the load acting on the surface mainly by a sort of membrane action acting through the entire surface. This causes all of the material to be more evenly stressed in compression or tension with little bending moment. The shell structure hence intrinsically derives its strength from its shape.

11.2 Types of shells

Shells may be divided basically into two classes—**singly curved** and **doubly curved**. Singly curved shells have curvature in only one direction and the simplest example of the singly curved shell is the **barrel vault** or the **cylindrical shell** shown in Fig. 164. The multiple barrel shells shown in Fig. 164 are supported on rigid end diaphragms and can also be looked upon as prismatic folded plates with an infinite number of plates. Another example of the singly curved shell is a **cone** which, as we have seen in 10.2 can be looked upon as a pyramidal folded plate structure with an infinite number of sides.

Doubly curved shells however, offer the most exciting possibilities. They can be of two types—**synclastic** shells and **anticlastic** shells. In synclastic shells, the principal curvatures are both on the same side of the surface as shown in Fig. 165a. In anticlastic shells, the principal curvatures are on opposite sides of the surface as shown in Fig. 165b. The **spherical dome** shell shown in Fig. 166 and the **tension membrane** shown in Fig. 167 are both examples of synclastic surfaces. The **conoid** shown in Fig. 168 and the

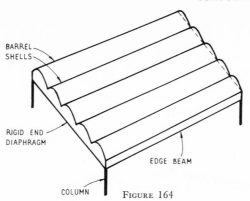

BARREL
SHELLS

RIGID END
DIAPHRAGM

EDGE BEAM

COLUMN

FIGURE 164

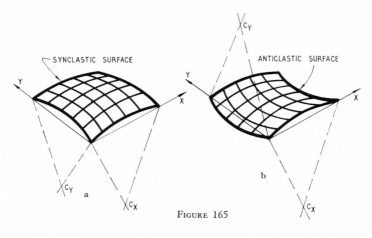

SYNCLASTIC SURFACE

ANTICLASTIC SURFACE

a

b

FIGURE 165

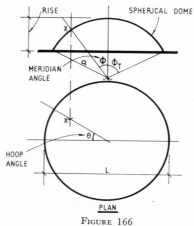

RISE

SPHERICAL DOME

MERIDIAN
ANGLE

HOOP
ANGLE

L

PLAN

FIGURE 166

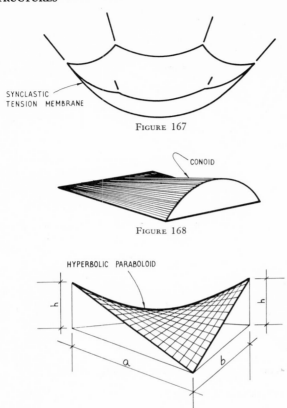

SYNCLASTIC
TENSION MEMBRANE

FIGURE 167

CONOID

FIGURE 168

HYPERBOLIC PARABOLOID

FIGURE 169

hyperbolic paraboloid shown in Fig. 169 are both examples of anticlastic surfaces, with the principal curvatures in opposite directions.

The three most important types of shell structures are undoubtedly the cylindrical or barrel shell, the spherical dome and the hyperbolic paraboloid (hypar) and these three types will now be considered in greater detail.

11.3 The barrel shell

Cylindrical barrel shells are shown in Fig. 164 and the close similarity between this type of shell and the prismatic folded plate structure was discussed in 11.2. In the analysis of the Vee type folded plate structure in 10.3 it was seen that the transverse action depends on the span of the transverse strip. As the number of plates in any one unit increases, the span becomes smaller and smaller until finally with an infinite number of plates, the span is zero. The transverse plate or strip action is therefore eliminated for long barrel shells, leaving only the overall longitudinal action of the structure to be considered.

For the overall longitudinal action it was seen in the design of the Vee type folded plate structure, that an internal unit in fact behaves like a beam of Vee (inverted) cross section spanning between the rigid end diaphragms. In a similar manner, the cylindrical barrel shell behaves like a beam of curved

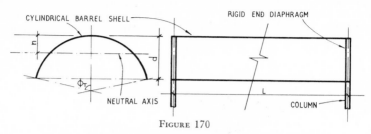

FIGURE 170

cross section as shown in Fig. 170. The position of the neutral axis and the second moment of area I_n about this axis can be determined as,

$$n = R \left(1 - \frac{\text{Sin } \phi_T}{\phi_T} \right) \dots\dots\dots\dots\dots\dots\dots\dots\dots\dots\dots\dots\dots\dots\dots\dots\dots\dots\dots\dots\dots\dots\dots\dots\dots\dots\dots\dots\dots\dots\dots\dots \quad 59$$

$$I_n = 2tR^3 \left(\frac{\phi_T}{2} + \frac{\text{Sin } 2\phi_T}{4} - \frac{\text{Sin}^2 \phi_T}{\phi_T} \right) \dots\dots\dots\dots\dots\dots\dots\dots\dots\dots\dots\dots\dots\dots \quad 60$$

where,

ϕ_T = central angle in radians as shown in Fig. 170

t = thickness of the shell

R = radius of the shell.

Since the shell behaves as a simply supported beam supported on the rigid end diaphragms, it follows that the maximum bending moment at the center is given by,

$$BM_{max} = \frac{wL^2}{8} = \frac{WL}{8}$$

By the use of the first of Eqns. 26 in 5.4, the maximum compressive stress in the concrete f_{bc} can be got as,

$$f_{bc} = \frac{M n}{I_n} \dots\dots\dots\dots\dots\dots\dots\dots\dots\dots\dots\dots\dots\dots\dots\dots\dots\dots\dots\dots\dots\dots\dots\dots\dots\dots\dots\dots\dots\dots\dots\dots\dots\dots \quad 61$$

If working stress design is used, this maximum compressive stress in the concrete must be less than that permissible for the concrete chosen. The thickness assumed in Eqn. 60 is then adequate. The area below the neutral axis is in tension and all the tension has to be taken by steel reinforcement.

Example 11.3.1

An area of 40 ft × 80 ft is to be roofed by four long cylindrical barrel shells over two spans of 40 ft each as shown in Fig. 171. The chord width is 10 ft and the rise of the barrels is 2 ft 6 in. If the shell thickness is 2 in. determine the maximum compressive stress in an internal barrel at positions of both maximum positive and maximum negative moment. The snow load is 25 lbs/sq ft.

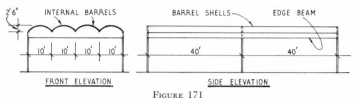

FIGURE 171

The radius of the cross section of each barrel shell can be determined as,

$$\mathbf{R}^2 = (\mathbf{R} - 2.5)^2 + 5^2$$

$$\mathbf{R}^2 = \mathbf{R}^2 - 5\mathbf{R} + 6.25 + 25$$

$$\mathbf{R} = \frac{31.25}{5} = 6.25 \text{ ft}$$

$$\text{Sin } \phi_T = \frac{5}{6.25} = 0.8000$$

$$\phi_T = 53° \; 6' \text{ say } 53$$

$$\phi_T = \frac{\pi \times 53}{180} = 0.925 \text{ radians}$$

For this value of ϕ_T, Sin $\phi_T = 0.7986$ and Cos $\phi_T = 0.6378$. Using Eqns. 59 and 60 we have,

$$\mathbf{n} = \mathbf{R} \left(1 - \frac{\text{Sin } \phi_T}{\phi_T} \right) = 6.25 \times \left(1 - \frac{0.7986}{0.925} \right) = 0.854 \text{ ft}$$

$$(\mathbf{d} - \mathbf{n}) = 2.500 - 0.854 = 1.646 \text{ ft}$$

$$\mathbf{I_n} = 2\mathbf{tR}^3 \left(\frac{\phi_T}{2} + \frac{\text{Sin } 2\phi_T}{4} - \frac{\text{Sin}^2 \phi_T}{\phi_T} \right)$$

$$\mathbf{I_n} = 2 \times 2 \times (6.25 \times 12)^3 \times \left(\frac{0.925}{2} + \frac{0.9613}{4} - \frac{0.7986^2}{0.925} \right)$$

$$\mathbf{I_n} = 2 \times 2 \times 75^3 \times (0.4625 + 0.2403 - 0.6895)$$

$$\mathbf{I_n} = 2 \times 2 \times 75^3 \times 0.0133 = 22440 \text{ in}^4$$

The section moduli for compression are therefore,

$$S_{c+} = \frac{I_n}{n} = \frac{22440}{0.854 \times 12} = 2189.7 \text{ in}^3$$

$$S_{c-} = \frac{I_n}{(d-n)} = \frac{22440}{1.646 \times 12} = 1136.1 \text{ in}^3.$$

The total loading on the barrel can be calculated as,

Self load $= 2 \times 12 = 24$ lbs/sq ft

Snow load $= 25$ lbs/sq ft

Self load $= R \times 2\phi_T \times 1 \times 24 = 6.25 \times 2 \times 0.925 \times 1 \times 24 = 277.5$ lbs/ft

Snow load $= 10 \times 1 \times 25 = 250$ lbs/ft

Total load $= 277.5 + 250 = 527.5$ lbs/ft

Since the barrels are absolutely symmetrical and the loading is absolutely symmetrical as well, the structure must have zero slope over the central diaphragm. Each internal barrel may therefore be looked upon as two propped cantilevers. The maximum bending moments for a propped cantilever are shown in Fig. 105 which gives,

$$M_{max} \text{ positive} = +\frac{9}{128} wL^2 = +\frac{9}{128} \times 527.5 \times 40^2 = +59344 \text{ lb ft}$$

$$M_{max} \text{ negative} = -\frac{wL^2}{8} = -\frac{1}{8} \times 527.5 \times 40^2 = -105500 \text{ lb ft}$$

The maximum longitudinal compressive stress in the middle of the barrel for the maximum positive moment is hence,

$$fc = \frac{M+}{S_{c+}} = \frac{59344 \times 12}{2189.7} = 325 \text{ psi}$$

The maximum longitudinal compressive stress over the central diaphragm for maximum negative moment is hence,

$$fc = \frac{M-}{S_{c-}} = \frac{105500 \times 12}{1136.1} = 1114 \text{ psi}$$

These compressive stresses are within the permissible limit for $fc' = 3000$ psi concrete and so the thickness is acceptable. With $fc' = 4000$ psi concrete, the barrels would be very safe.

It should be noted here that the calculation for I_n is very sensitive to small errors or approximations and hence care should be taken in the calculations. It may also be noted that the longitudinal beam action and the longitudinal stresses determined are valid only for long barrels, where the $\dfrac{\text{span}}{\text{chord}}$ ratio is at least greater than 2. For short barrels, a transverse membrane action does take place and can be important.

11.4 The spherical dome

The spherical dome is a superb example of a doubly curved synclastic shell structure that has been known since early times as a very efficient structural form. Masonry domes, with the material entirely in compression have been built for hundreds of years. They depend for their stability on their weight and are therefore naturally quite massive. Modern spherical domes in concrete are however thin shell structures and the small thickness introduces the possibility of buckling. This buckling has therefore to be checked and very often is the governing criterion of design in the determination of the thickness.

Consider the spherical dome shown in Fig. 166. There are two main directions—the meridian direction and the hoop direction. The angle ϕ is called the meridian angle. If the dome is hemispherical then $\phi = 90°$. The angle θ is called the hoop angle. By specifying the angles ϕ and θ, any point on the shell surface can be exactly located.

It has been mentioned that the shell dome propagates load towards the supports by a membrane action through the shell. This membrane analysis can be determined easily and is an accurate representation of the behavior of the shell provided the boundary edge of the dome is on rollers as shown in Fig. 172. If the boundary is not on rollers, but pinned or fixed as shown in

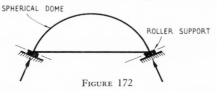

FIGURE 172

Fig. 173, bending moments arise which require a thickening of the shell towards the base. It has been found however, that this boundary edge disturbance is localised and the bending moments die out rapidly towards the crown. This is shown for the fixed edge in Fig. 173a and for the pinned edge in Fig. 173b. The membrane action is still reasonably valid towards the crown of the dome.

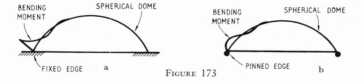

FIGURE 173

The membrane forces for the spherical shell dome under dead load has been determined as,

$$N\phi = -aq \left(\frac{1}{1 + Cos\ \phi} \right) \dotfill 62$$

$$N\theta = +aq \left(\frac{1}{1 + Cos\ \phi} - Cos\ \phi \right) \dotfill 63$$

where,

$$N\phi = \text{meridianal force in lbs/ft}$$

$$N\theta = \text{hoop or tangential force in lbs/ft}$$

$$a = \text{radius of the shell dome in ft}$$

$$q = \text{intensity of the dead load or self load} \\ \text{in lbs/sq ft of surface area}$$

The negative sign to the force denotes compression whilst the positive sign denotes tension. By inserting the appropriate value of ϕ, the meridian or hoop forces can be determined at any horizontal ring level.

At the crown $\phi = 0$,

$$N\phi = -\frac{aq}{2}$$

$$\dotfill 64$$

$$N\theta = -\frac{aq}{2}$$

For a hemispherical dome at the boundary edge $\phi = \frac{\pi}{2}$,

$$N\phi = -aq$$

$$\dotfill 65$$

$$N\theta = +aq$$

The meridian force increases continuously from the crown towards the base edge but the hoop force changes from compressive to tensile. It can be shown that at $\phi = 51° 50'$, the membrane hoop force is zero.

Under a snow load of **p** lbs/sq ft on the plan area, the membrane analysis gives,

$$N\phi = -\frac{ap}{2}$$

$$\dotfill 66$$

$$N\theta = -\frac{ap\ Cos\ 2\phi}{2}$$

At the crown $\phi = 0$,

$$N\phi = -\frac{ap}{2}$$

                                                                                67

$$N\theta = -\frac{ap}{2}$$

At the boundary edge for a hemispherical dome where $\phi = \frac{\pi}{2}$,

$$N\phi = -\frac{ap}{2}$$

                                                                                68

$$N\theta = +\frac{ap}{2}$$

The meridian force stays constant under snow load from the crown to the base, but the hoop force once again changes from compressive to tensile. This time the position of zero hoop force is at $\phi = 45°$. The above analysis for both dead and snow load implies that for a shallow dome, the base is still under compression but that for a deep dome, the base is in hoop tension. A base ring has therefore to be provided with sufficient reinforcement for all the tension force to be taken only by the steel.

The buckling of thin walled shell domes is very important and should be considered by the Architect in his estimation of the thickness of the dome. The load at which the shell will buckle under vertical loading is given by,

$$p_{cr} = CE \left(\frac{t}{a} \right)^2$$

                                                                                69

where,

$p_{cr} =$ critical buckling stress in lbs/sq in.

$E =$ modulus of elasticity of the material in lbs/sq in.

$t =$ thickness of the spherical shell dome in in.

$a =$ radius of the spherical shell dome in in.

$C =$ a constant which varies, depending on the type of shell and the material, but which may be assumed to be about 0.20.

The factor of safety against buckling checked only against vertical loading should be at least about 6 to 7.

Example 11.4.1

Determine the average thickness of a spherical shell dome with a span of

100 ft and a maximum rise at the crown of 20 ft 9 in. The shell dome has to withstand a snow load of 30 lbs/sq ft.

The spherical shell dome has been shown in Fig. 166. The span is 100 ft and the rise is 20 ft 9 in. and the radius of the shell **a** can be calculated as,

$$\mathbf{a}^2 = (\mathbf{a} - 20.75)^2 + 50^2$$

$$\mathbf{a}^2 = \mathbf{a}^2 - 41.50\mathbf{a} + 430.56 + 2500.00$$

$$\mathbf{a} = \frac{2930.56}{41.50} = 70.62 \text{ ft}$$

The total meridianal angle ϕ_T can be determined as,

$$\mathbf{Sin}\ \phi_T = \frac{50}{70.62} = 0.7080$$

$$\phi_T = 45°\ 4'\ \text{say } 45°$$

Assume that the thickness of the shell is 2 in. with a finishing load of 1 in. The dead load on the shell can be got as,

Self load $= 12 \times 2 = 24$ lbs/sq ft

Finishing load $= 12 \times 1 = 12$ lbs/sq ft

Total dead load $\mathbf{q} = 36$ lbs/sq ft of surface area

Snow load $= 30$ lbs/sq ft of plan area

Check for buckling

The use of Eqn. 69 gives,

$$\mathbf{p}_{cr} = \mathbf{CE}\left(\frac{\mathbf{t}}{\mathbf{a}}\right)^2 = 0.20 \times 3 \times 10^6 \times \left(\frac{2}{70.62 \times 12}\right)^2$$

$$\mathbf{p}_{cr} = 3.34 \text{ psi}$$

The critical buckling load in lbs/sq ft is hence,

$$\mathbf{P}_{cr} = \mathbf{p}_{cr} \times 144 = 3.34 \times 144 = 480.96 \text{ lbs/sq ft}$$

The factor of safety against buckling is therefore,

$$\text{Factor of safety} = \frac{480.96}{36 + 30} = 7.29$$

This is quite acceptable.

The meridian and hoop membrane stresses at the crown and at the base can be very easily calculated by first calculating the membrane forces. The use of Eqns. 62 and 63 for the dead load and Eqns. 66 for the snow load give,

For dead load at the crown,

$$N\phi = - 1271.2 \text{ lb ft/ft}$$
$$N\theta = - 1271.2 \text{ lb ft/ft}$$

For dead load at the base,

$$N\phi = -1489.3 \text{ lb ft/ft}$$
$$N\theta = - 308.4 \text{ lb ft/ft}$$

For snow load at the crown,

$$N\phi = - 1059.3 \text{ lb ft/ft}$$
$$N\theta = - 1059.3 \text{ lb ft/ft}$$

For snow load at the base,

$$N\phi = - 1059.3 \text{ lb ft/ft}$$
$$N\theta = 0$$

The membrane forces under the two loadings can now be added and the stresses calculated as,

$$\textbf{Meridian stress at the crown} = \frac{- 1271.2 - 1059.3}{12 \times 2} = - 97.1 \text{ psi}$$

$$\textbf{Hoop stress at the crown} = \frac{- 1271.2 - 1059.3}{12 \times 2} = - 97.1 \text{ psi}$$

$$\textbf{Meridian stress at the base} = \frac{- 1489.3 - 1059.3}{12 \times 2} = - 106.2 \text{ psi}$$

$$\textbf{Hoop stress at the base} = \frac{- 308.4 + 0}{12 \times 2} = - 12.9 \text{ psi}$$

Two important conclusions can be drawn from this membrane analysis. The first is that the membrane stresses both in the meridian as also in the hoop directions, at the crown and at the base of the dome, are very small compared to the permissible compressive stress for the concrete chosen. Secondly, in this particular case, no tension develops anywhere. The only reinforcement that is necessary is secondary temperature and shrinkage wire mesh reinforcement steel placed at the center of the 2 in. thickness. This secondary steel should be about 0.2% of the concrete area. For a deeper dome, tension will develop in the hoop direction and must be taken by steel reinforcement. It should be noted that the bending analysis, which is very complex, has not been carried out for the base of the dome. A certain gradual thickening of the dome at the base would be necessary to take this bending into account. The wind load on the dome has also not been considered and for a more exact analysis, taking these considerations into account, the

Architect is referred to the author's other book **Structural Design with Plastics** which deals with the principles involved and the exact design of spherical domes.

11.5 Hyperbolic paraboloid shells

The basic element of a hypar has been shown in Fig. 169. This type of shell, as has been stated, is an anticlastic shell where the principal curvatures are in opposite directions. The shell surface is derived by the movement of one parabola on another parabola of opposite curvature. It can also be looked upon as the movement of a line on two skew lines. This latter method of generating the surface implies that the formwork for a hyperbolic paraboloid can be built out of straight elements. This makes the formwork relatively simple.

The shell surface under the vertical uniformly distributed loading is extremely efficient in propagating the load to the supports. The shell behaves as a compression membrane with an arch action in one direction, and as a tension membrane with a cable action in the other. Further the compression membrane is stabilised and prevented from buckling by the support it gets from the tension membrane. Since the parabolic arch, as we have seen in 3.9, is in pure compression under uniformly distributed vertical loading, the

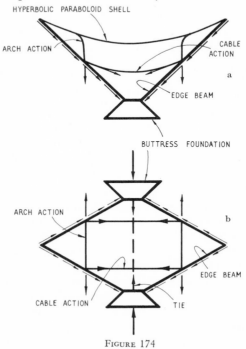

FIGURE 174

compression membrane is under a pure compression. Since the parabolic cable, as we have seen in 3.10, is under pure tension, the tension membrane is also under a pure tension. The entire surface is therefore under pure compressive and tensile forces with complete absence of moments—under a uniformly distributed vertical load.

The propagation of the load by the surface as a membrane towards the supports is shown in Fig. 174. The arch action of the compression membrane causes a thrust on the edge beams in one direction as shown. The cable action of the tension membrane causes a pull on the edge beam at right angles. The resultant of these forces is an axial force that flows down the edge beam towards the foundations. The edge beams hence pick up all these axial forces from the continuous connection with the membrane and transmit them to the foundations. At the foundations, these axial thrusts have to be resisted either by the provision of a tie or by buttressing as shown in Fig. 174.

The membrane compressive and tensile forces in a hypar can be got as,

$$C = -\frac{wab}{2h}$$

$$T = +\frac{wab}{2h}$$
                                                                                                    70

where,

> a, b and h are the dimensions of the hypar as shown in Fig. 169,
>
> $w =$ loading in lbs/sq ft.

The forces in the edge beams can be obtained as,

$$F_1 = \frac{wab}{2h}\sqrt{a^2 + h^2}$$

$$F_2 = \frac{wab}{2h}\sqrt{b^2 + h^2}$$
                                                                                                    71

It should be noted here again that the shell is under tension and compression membrane forces only under a uniformly distributed vertical loading. Under any other loading, such as a point load, bending moments will arise. Since the edge beams have to take large compressive forces, they are larger than the shell membrane itself thereby imposing line loads along the edges. This leads to a thickening of the shell towards the edge as shown in Fig. 175. The enclosure of a hypar may also present additional problems. The enclosure if carried out independently is the best solution as thereby no additional loads are imposed on the edge.

The design of a simple hypar can now be easily carried out.

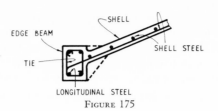

FIGURE 175

Example 11.5.1

Design a simple single hyperbolic paraboloid shell of the type shown in Fig. 169, for the following dimensions:

$$a = 30 \text{ ft}$$

$$b = 40 \text{ ft}$$

$$h = 20 \text{ ft}$$

The snow load is 35 lbs/sq ft. Determine also the sizes of the edge beams of the structure.

Assume that the shell thickness is 2 in. with a 10 lbs/sq ft load for finishing, waterproofing, etc. The total load on the hypar can hence be calculated as,

$$\text{Self load} = 2 \times 12 = 24 \text{ lbs/sq ft}$$

$$\text{Finishing, waterproofing, etc.} = 10 \text{ lbs/sq ft}$$

$$\text{Snow load} = 35 \text{ lbs/sq ft}$$

$$\text{Total load} = 69 \text{ lbs/sq ft}$$

In a shell of this type, the actual surface area is not vastly greater than the plan area and so a simple addition of the loads is acceptable.

The forces in the membrane can be got by the use of Eqns. 70 as,

$$C = T = \mp \frac{wab}{2h} = \mp \frac{69 \times 30 \times 40}{2 \times 20} = \mp 2070 \text{ lbs/ft}$$

The compressive stress in the membrane is hence,

$$fc = \frac{2070}{12 \times 2} = 86.25 \text{ psi}$$

This is very low and quite acceptable. The only reinforcement needed in the arch direction is secondary temperature and shrinkage steel of about 0.2% of the concrete area. Wire mesh reinforcement at the center of the shell thickness could be placed very conveniently. The tension membrane force is also 2070 lbs/ft. This tensile force has to be taken entirely by the steel reinforcement. It will however be found that the actual steel required is very nominal and the wire mesh fabric placed at the center of the shell thickness will adequately serve in both directions. The diameter of the bars forming the wire mesh and their spacing would have to be appropriately chosen by the Structural Engineer to ensure that the mesh that he actually chooses satisfies and provides him with an adequate area of steel in both directions.

The forces in the edge beams can be determined by the use of Eqns. 71 as,

$$F_1 = \frac{wab}{2h} \sqrt{a^2 + h^2} = 2070 \times \sqrt{30^2 + 20^2} = 74635 \text{ lbs}$$

$$F_2 = \frac{wab}{2h} \sqrt{b^2 + h^2} = 2070 \times \sqrt{40^2 + 20^2} = 92573 \text{ lbs}$$

The design of the edge beams can also be easily carried out. The beams are compressive members, but they are prevented from buckling because they are restrained by the membrane along the entire length. They can hence be designed as short, tied columns as outlined in 5.12.

The live load is almost the same as the dead load and so the ultimate load on the edge beam can be determined as,

$$P_u = \frac{1.4 + 1.7}{2} \times 92573 = 1.55 \times 92573 = 143488 \text{ lbs}$$

With $fc' = 4000$ psi and $f_y = 60000$ psi and with the use of Eqn. 45 we have for a 4 in. $\times$ 10 in. size of edge beam,

$$P_u = \phi \left[0.85fc' \times (A_g - A_s) + A_s \, f_y \right]$$

$$143488 = 0.70 \times \left[0.85 \times 4000 \times (4 \times 10 - A_s) + A_s \, 60000 \right]$$

This gives $A_s = 1.22$ sq in.

Use #6 bars, area of each bar $= 0.44$ sq in.

$$\text{Total number of bars required} = \frac{1.22}{0.44} = 2.8 \text{ say 4 nos.}$$

The other edge beam has a lesser value of force in it. Use the same size of edge beam. In the above design, the steel could be cut down a little if desired. As an alternative a 4 in. $\times$ 8 in. edge beam with 4 nos. of #6 bars would also be acceptable.

Hyperbolic paraboloids do not necessarily have to be used singly. They can be used in sets of four as shown in Fig. 176. The four hypars can be supported on four columns as shown in Fig. 176a. The forces in the edge beams are shown by the arrows. Two edge beams of each hypar react against other edge beams, whilst the other two edge beams of each hypar react against the columns. The tops of the columns have therefore to be tied as

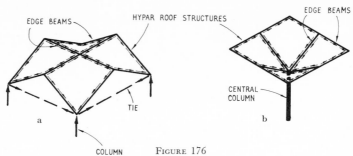

FIGURE 176

shown in Fig. 176a. The arrangement shown in Fig. 176b consists of four hypars supported on a central column. In this umbrella type of roof structure, two edge beams of each hypar react against each other on the central column whilst the other two edge beams of each hypar react against each other—but are in tension. For these edge beams, the total tensile force has to be taken entirely by the steel reinforcement in the edge beam. The concrete cannot be assumed to take any tension and so merely provides cover for the steel reinforcement.

In the cases discussed above, the design of the structure would still be carried out by designing an individual hypar as considered in this article.

11.6 Similarity between folded plates and shells

This chapter on shell structures cannot be closed without commenting on the very close similarities between folded plates and shells. Some of these similarities have already been discussed in the design of cylindrical barrel shells. If the number of plates in any folded plate structure is large, the structure may be approximated to a shell and analysed as such with reasonably accurate results. The same is true in reverse as well and a shell may be approximated by a folded plate structure if it is more convenient to do so. The distinction between folded plates and shells may at times be both architecturally and structurally a little artificial. Consider the folded plate conical dome that has been shown in Fig. 159. If the two plates in any unit were to be replaced by a singly curved shell, the structure becomes a conical shell dome as shown dotted in Fig. 177. If the apex of the shell dome is now

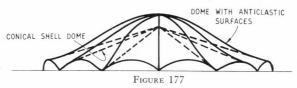

FIGURE 177

raised, the structure becomes a dome shell with anticlastic surfaces. The three structures may lie in different classifications, but have both architecturally and structurally a lot in common.

Problems for solution

Example 1: For the Architectural designs arrived at in your Studio courses, examine the possibility of providing and integrating shell structures of various types into the designs. Verbalise the load propagation through the structure. Attempt, if possible, an analysis of the shell and determine an approximate thickness for it.

Example 2: A spherical dome in concrete has a span of 120 ft and a maximum rise of 20 ft. The average thickness of the shell is 2 in. If the total vertical load (dead + snow) is 50 lbs/sq ft determine the factor of safety against buckling, under the vertical load. $E = 3 \times 10^6$ psi.

Ans: Factor of safety $= 4.8$.

Example 3: Redesign the hyperbolic paraboloid of Example 11.5.1 in timber. If the total load is still assumed to be 69 lbs/sq ft and the maximum compressive stress in the timber is to be limited to 400 psi, determine the approximate thickness of the timber planks for the hypar.

Ans: 0.43 in. say ½ in. thick.

Chapter 12
SPACE STRUCTURES

12.1 The space structure

Of all the structural systems that have been considered, the space structure is the one most suitable for roofing the largest spans and carrying the heaviest loads. It can be built in timber but is ideally suited for steel or aluminum. The structure consists of a number of members such as angles, tubes, or other shapes, connected together at the joints to form a three dimensional structure. Such a structure can be single layered for relatively small spans or double layered for the largest spans. Some single layer domes are shown in Figs. 178-180. The **Schwedler** dome, shown in Fig. 178a consists of ribs and

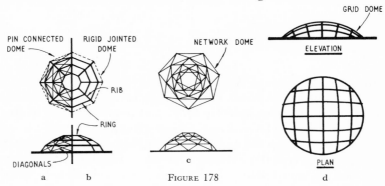

FIGURE 178

rings with diagonals in every panel. The joints may be assumed as pin connected. If only one diagonal is used in every panel, the rather long member must be capable of taking compression as well as tension and this makes the member large in size. Two diagonals may therefore be used, with only one tension diagonal being assumed as effective. This is shown in Fig. 178a. If the diagonals are objectionable and are to be eliminated completely, the joints must be made rigid for a stable structure and the dome is

then called a stiff or **rigid jointed dome** as shown in Fig. 178b. Another type
of single layer dome is the **network dome** as shown in Fig. 178c. The network dome does not have ribs and rings since every ring level is rotated with
respect to adjoining ones. The network dome is stable only under an odd
number of sides. The grid dome is shown in Fig. 178d.

Another type of single layer dome that has been extensively built in
timber is the **lamella dome** shown in Fig. 179. The lamella dome shown in

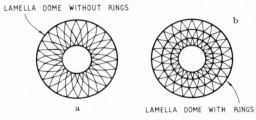

LAMELLA DOME WITHOUT RINGS

b

a   LAMELLA DOME WITH RINGS

FIGURE 179

Fig. 179a does not have horizontal ring members. In such a dome, the timber
roof sheathing is assumed to act integrally with the dome thereby providing
stability without ring members. The single layer geodesic dome is shown in
Fig. 180.

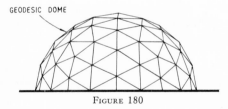

GEODESIC DOME

FIGURE 180

Three dimensional single layer space frames can be used for a variety of
shapes such as arches or barrel vaults, hyperbolic paraboloids, conoids, etc.

The space structure becomes very strong and very suitable for roofing big
spans when it is double layered with a large structural depth. Such a space
structure can be used as a flat roof to cover large areas. It is then also termed
as a **space deck**. A typical space deck is shown in Fig. 181. The structure is
supported on just four columns to give long, clear, unobstructed spans. It is
suitable only in steel and aluminum. Double layered space structures with
large structural depths can also be curved and used as domes or arched structures to cover the largest spans.

12.2 The analysis of a space structure

The analysis of a three dimensional single layer or double layer space
structure can only be properly carried out by the use of the computer. The
very large number of joints and members that form the structure can make

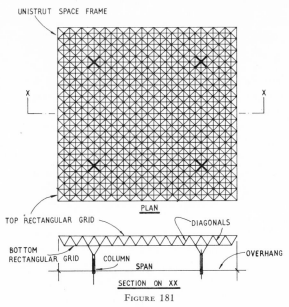

FIGURE 181

it several hundred times—and in the case of very large structures even several thousand times—statically indeterminate or redundant. Any attempt to analyse the structure by hand calculation is just not feasible. For the analysis of such structures, the computer has proved to be an invaluable tool. The program that needs to be fed into the computer for the analysis of a space structure is itself very complex and takes many years to develop, so as to be general enough to be applicable to a large number of cases. Once such a general program is available however, the structure itself becomes unimportant because all that the program requires is certain basic information on the structure. This information concerns the number and coordinates of the joints, the number of members and the way in which they are oriented between the joints, the approximate sizes of the members, the loads to be applied, etc. All this information which is basic data concerning the geometry of the structure and its loading is fed into the computer. The general program for the analysis now analyses the particular structure, for which the data has been fed into it, to yield the final answers which then have to be correctly interpreted to yield the final design. The process of feeding into the computer the required data for a particular structure that the Architect wishes to design is termed as **Coding.** Coding is in fact very easy and does not require any special knowledge by the Architect of the computer or the program for the analysis of the structure. All that the Architect should be able to do is to peruse a Coding Manual over a weekend! Several service bureaus have computer programs available for use by clients (the Architect) if he is prepared to Code his own structure (with help from the service bureau if needed) and pay the service bureau its fees for running the program.

12.3 STRUDL

The program that the author uses for his own work was developed by MIT for IBM and is called **STRUDL**. STRUDL stands for **St**ructural **D**esign **L**anguage and comes in two parts STRUDL 1 and STRUDL 2. STRUDL 1 is for the analysis of skeletal space structures with discrete members whilst STRUDL 2 is for the analysis of continuum structures such as concrete shells, shear walls, arch dams, etc.

STRUDL 1 is very valuable to the Architect for the analysis and design of his space structure, providing that he can code his own structure using the STRUDL Coding Manual and providing that he can then interpret correctly the results, when supplied to him by the service bureau. This Chapter is no substitute for the reading and study of the STRUDL Coding Manual since all of the Manual could hardly be discussed here. Nevertheless a basic elementary knowledge of STRUDL Coding can be easily appreciated and two simple problems are taken here for that purpose. Every line in the Coding has been explained for ease of understanding.

Example 12.3.1

Code the two bay, pitched roof, plane portal frame shown in Fig. 182 for the STRUDL 1 program.

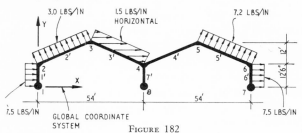

FIGURE 182

The structure shown in Fig. 182 is acted upon by a wind loading. The first step in the Coding is to select an overall or **global coordinate system** of axes. The origin is selected at the joint 1 and the global coordinate axes **X** and **Y** are shown in Fig. 182. The joints of the structure have now to be numbered and the joint numbers 1, 2, 3 etc, are shown in Fig. 182. The members now have also to be numbered and the member numbers 1', 2', 3' etc, have also been shown in Fig. 182. In addition to the global coordinate system, a local or **member coordinate system** has also to be defined. Such a member coordinate system for any member is shown in Fig. 183 with the **X** axis lying along the length of the member. The structure can now be coded and the Coding is shown below:

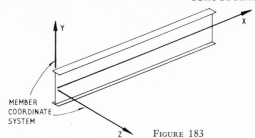

FIGURE 183

STRUDL 'EX 1' 'PLANE FRAME'

TYPE PLANE FRAME

$ FOR THE SAKE OF CLARITY, ABBREVIATED COMMANDS
WILL NOT BE USED IN THIS EXAMPLE

JOINT COORDINATES

1 X   0. Y   0. SUPPORT

2 X   0. Y 150.

3 X   324. Y 294.

4 X   648. Y 150.

5 X   972. Y 294.

6 X 1296. Y 150.

7 X 1296. Y   0. SUPPORT

8 X   648. Y   0. SUPPORT

JOINT RELEASES

1 7 8 MOMENT Z

MEMBER INCIDENCES

1 1 2

2 2 3

3 3 4

4 4 5

5 5 6

6 7 6

7 8 4

MEMBER PROPERTIES PRISMATIC

1 TO 7 AX 8.9 IZ 290.1

CONSTANTS

E 30000000.0 ALL

G 12000000.0 ALL

LOADING 1 'WIND LOAD'

MEMBER LOADS

1.6 FORCE X GLOBAL UNIFORM W 7.5

2 FORCE Y UNIFORM W 3.0 $ MEMBERS 2 AND 5 ARE LOADED
IN LOCAL AXES DIRECTIONS

3 FORCE X GLOBAL UNIFORM W 1.5

5 FORCE Y UNIFORM W 7.2

LOADING LIST 1

STIFFNESS ANALYSIS

LIST FORCES REACTIONS DISPLACEMENTS LOADS

Each line in the above Coding will now be explained in detail.

Line 1: This gives the title of the project which the computer will print out with the results.

Line 2: The type of structure is specified here as 'PLANE FRAME'. Other types of structures that can be specified to the computer are 'PLANE TRUSS', 'PLANE GRID', 'SPACE TRUSS' and 'SPACE FRAME'.

Line 3: The $ sign indicates a 'COMMENT'. Whatever appears after the $ sign in that line is printed out as it stands. In this case we are reminding ourselves that abbreviated commands are not being used. An experienced Coder could use allowable abbreviated commands such as SPA FRA for SPACE FRAME or JOI COO for JOINT COORDINATES, etc.

Line 4: The joint coordinates in inches are now given to the computer. Since no units are specified, the computer assumes that all coordinates are in inches only.

Line 5: The joint 1 has an X coordinate = 0 in. and a Y coordinate = 0 in. It is also a support. The word SUPPORT could have been abbreviated to S.

Line 6-12: The joint coordinates in in. for all the joints are given. The joints 7 and 8 are also supports.

Line 13: The program in the computer assumes that all joints are fixed unless otherwise stated. This line informs the computer that certain joints will have certain releases in specific directions.

Line 14: The joints 1, 7 and 8 are shown as pinned in Fig. 182. The moment about the Z axis (which runs out of the plane of the paper) must be zero.

Line 15: The joints have been specified but the description of the geometry of the space structure is not complete without complete knowledge of the number and arrangement of bars between the joints. This is termed as 'MEMBER INCIDENCES'.

Line 16: The numbers 1 1 2 specify that the member 1 (shown in Fig. 182 as 1′ for purposes of clarity) lies between joint 1 and joint 2. The origin of the member coordinate system of axes for the member is at joint 1.

Line 17-22: The member incidences for the remaining members 2′ to 7′ are specified. For instance, the numbers 7 8 4 specify that the member 7 runs from joint 8 to joint 4. The origin of the member coordinate system of axes for this member is hence chosen at 8.

Line 23: The properties of the member have now to be inputed. These are estimated before the analysis is commenced and checked after the design is complete. If the members have the same section throughout their length, the members are prismatic and are so stated. If however, the members were tapering, with varying properties along the length, the statement would have read 'MEMBER PROPERTIES VARIABLE'.

Line 24: The properties for all the members 1′ to 7′ are assumed to be the same. The cross sectional area AX is assumed to be 8.9 sq in. and the second moment of area in the plane of bending about the global coordinate Z axis, $IZ = 290.1$ in.^{4}

Line 25: The modulus of elasticity E and the modulus of rigidity G (the shear modulus) for the material of which the structure is made have now to be specified. These are naturally CONSTANTS for the structure.

Line 26: The modulus of elasticity of the material $E = 30 \times 10^6$ psi.

Line 27: The modulus of rigidity or the shear modulus of the material $G = 12 \times 10^6$ psi.

Line 28: The loading on the structure has to be specified. The computer will print out WIND LOAD on the output.

Line 29: The loading on this particular structure acts only on the members and is hence specified as MEMBER LOADS. There are no JOINT LOADS in this problem.

Line 30: The member loads for the members 1 and 6 (members 1' and 6' in Fig. 182) are specified in the global coordinate system. The load in this case is a FORCE and acts in the X direction and is uniformly distributed with a value of 7.5 lbs/in.

Line 31: The member load for member 2' is specified in the member coordinate system because it is easier to do so. It acts in the direction of the local Y axis. The comment statement after the $ sign explains this.

Line 32-33: The member loads on members 3' and 5' are given.

Line 34: The computer is asked to list or identify the loading for which the analysis is being carried out. In this case it is only WIND LOAD.

Line 35: The stiffness method of analysis is to be used for the analysis of the structure and this is specified.

Line 36: The computer is asked to output all results of FORCES at the joints, REACTIONS at the supports, DISPLACEMENTS of the joints and as a check joint LOADS. These joint LOADS should be zero since in this problem, no loads have been applied at the joints.

The service bureau transfers this coding into punched cards which are then fed into the computer as data. The powerful STRUDL 1 program analyses this particular structure and the computer prints out the results. These results are then sent back to the Architect or Engineer who has now

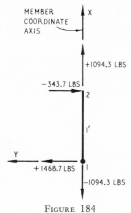

FIGURE 184

to interpret them correctly. A partial output for the Example 12.3.1 is given here.

PROBLEM — EX 1 TITLE — PLANE FRAME

ACTIVE UNITS INCH LB RAD DEGF SEC ACTIVE STRUCTURE
  TYPE PLANE FRAME

ACTIVE COORDINATE AXES X Y

LOADING—1 WIND LOAD

MEMBER FORCES

MEMBER	JOINT	FORCE		MOMENT BENDING
		AXIAL	SHEAR Y	Z
1	1	−1094.3086	1468.6958	000000.000
1	2	1094.3086	−343.6958	135929.375
2	2	−758.5142	−860.4038	−135929.375
2	3	758.5142	−203.2727	19433.641

ETC

ETC

In the first line of the output, the title is printed out. In the second line, the computer has printed out the units with which it has been working. No units had been specified in the Coding. It can be seen that only the axial force in the X direction, the shear force in the Y direction and the bending moment about the Z axis are outputed. This is because the structure is a two dimensional plane frame structure.

At joint 1 of member 1′, the axial force is given as −1094.3086 lbs. At joint 2 of member 1′, the axial force is given as 1094.3086 lbs. The reason is shown in Fig. 184. It can be seen that the signs of the forces are related to the positive directions of the member coordinate axes. The member 1′ is in tension as shown in Fig. 184.

As a final check, let us calculate the moment at the joint 2 and compare it to the value of 135929.375 lb in. as outputed by the computer. Referring to Fig. 184 and working in ft units we have,

$$\mathbf{M}_2 = 1468.6958 \times 12.5 - 7.5 \times 12 \times \frac{12.5^2}{2} = 18358.7 - 7031.3 = 11327.4 \, \text{lb ft.}$$

Converting this to lb in. units we have,

$$\mathbf{M}_2 = 11327.4 \times 12 = 135928.8 \, \text{lb in.}$$

The computer results are actually printed to seven places of the decimal but have been rounded off for ease of calculation and the check is therefore perfectly acceptable.

Example 12.3.2

Code the simple space tripod shown in Fig. 185 for STRUDL 1. The structure is required to be analysed for the two loading conditions separately and a third condition which is 100 K vertical + 150 K horizontal at the apex.

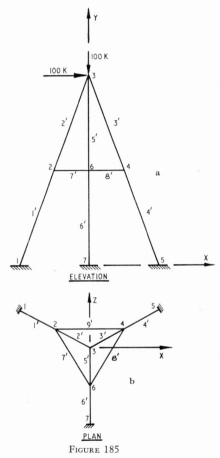

ELEVATION

PLAN

FIGURE 185

The global coordinate system and the numbering arrangement for joints and members is shown in Fig. 185. The Coding is shown below:

STRUDL 'TRIPOD'

$ ABBREVIATED COMMANDS WILL BE USED

TYPE SPA FRA

UNI KIP DEG

JOI COO

1	−173.2	0.	100.	S
2	−86.6	250.	50.	
3	0.	500.	0.	
4	86.6	250.	50.	
5	173.2	0.	100.	S
6	0.	250.	−100.	
7	0.	0.	−200.	S

MEM INC

1 1 2

2 2 3

3 4 3

4 5 4

5 6 3

6 7 6

7 2 6

8 6 4

9 4 2

MEM PROP PRISMATIC

1 TO 9 AX 8.9 IX 21.1 IY 30.0 IZ 290.1 $ THESE VALUES HAVE
BEEN CHOSEN FOR ILLUSTRATIVE PURPOSES ONLY

CONSTANTS

E 30000. ALL

G 12000. ALL

BETA 90.0 ALL BUT 348.6 7 8 9

LOA 1

JOI LOA

3 FOR Y −100.

LOA 2

JOI LOA

3 FOR X 100.

LOADING COMBINATION 3 COMBINE 1 1.0 2 1.5

LOA LIS ALL

STIFFN A

LIST REA DISP

Only those commands which are different from Example 12.3.1 will be explained here.

Line 3: The structure is a SPACE FRAME.

Line 4: The units are specified as being KIPS and DEGREES. This has to be stated for otherwise the units would have been LB and RADIANS. The unit of length is still INCHES however.

Line 26 and 27: The constants are given in KIPS and not in LB.

Line 28: The angle BETA is shown in Fig. 186. It is defined as being 90° for the leg members but as 348.6° for members 7', 8' and 9'.

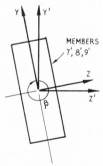

FIGURE 186

Line 30: In this problem we have joint loads.

Line 31: The loads are in the global coordinate system. At joint 3, the vertical load is 100 K in a direction opposed to the positive direction of the Y axis.

Line 35: This command combines the first loading with 1.5 times the second loading.

It should be repeated here emphatically that this Chapter is no substitute for the Coding Manual for STRUDL 1 and the Architect is strongly advised to obtain the Manual from IBM and study it carefully.

12.4 **Connections**

A space structure, as we have seen, consists of a large number of members connected together at the joints—which may be several hundred or even several thousand in number. It is easy to see therefore, that an inefficient connection—either in an aesthetic or in an engineering or economic sense— being multiplied so many times over can destroy completely the efficiency of the space structure. Good connections are vital to good design. Several different types are available, each being protected by patents and available under various trade names. One such connection for the **UNISTRUT** system in steel is shown in Fig. 187a. The space frame members which are sheet steel channels are bolted to the pressed steel plate. The roofing of the structure with a metal deck is shown in Fig. 187b. A light gage steel deck can be spot welded to the lip of the channel that forms the top chord of the space frame. Lightweight insulating concrete $2\frac{1}{2}$ in. thick can be poured in place on to the steel deck and topped off with a built up roof, as discussed in Chapter 6. Several other roofing and connection details are available in the manufacturer's literature.

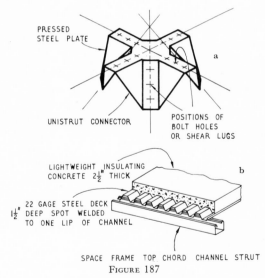

PRESSED STEEL PLATE

a

UNISTRUT CONNECTOR

POSITIONS OF BOLT HOLES OR SHEAR LUGS

LIGHTWEIGHT INSULATING CONCRETE $2\frac{1}{2}$" THICK

b

22 GAGE STEEL DECK $1\frac{1}{2}$" DEEP SPOT WELDED TO ONE LIP OF CHANNEL

SPACE FRAME TOP CHORD CHANNEL STRUT

FIGURE 187

Another excellent connector for the **Triodetic** system in aluminum is shown in Fig. 188. The connector consists of an aluminum hub with slotted keyways. The aluminum tubes of the space structure, which come into the hub at different angles, all have their ends crimped so that they slide easily into the slots of the hub. Washers at top and bottom prevent the tubes from being drawn out of the hub. The washers are themselves held in place by a bolt which is slipped through the central hole in the hub and locked with a nut. This has been shown in Fig. 188. The entire space structure fits together neatly and easily. The exact angles of the tubes and the crimping that is necessary are worked out by a computer from the geometry of the structure and the coordinates of the nodal points.

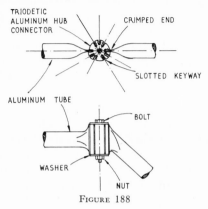

FIGURE 188

It is a little unlikely—unless it is a tremendously important structure—that the Architect will choose to design his own space structural system with his own connections. It is more likely that he will seek a readily available structural system that suits his purposes. Several such systems are available on the market and the Architect is well advised to consider them all carefully, particularly from the point of aesthetics and economics.

Chapter 13
TENSION STRUCTURES

13.1 Cable nets

The structural behavior of a single cable has been studied in Chapter 3 and it was seen that the cable carried the external loads applied to it in pure tension. Since the cable is very strong in tension, this was a very efficient structural system. The same principle is used by a cable net structure to roof large spans. The cable net, shown in Fig. 189, carries the roof and snow loads

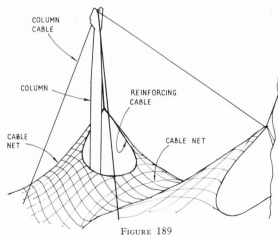

FIGURE 189

by tensile forces in the individual cables, thereby functioning as a tension membrane. It was also seen in 3.10 that the tension in the cable reduces with a larger sag. The same principle operates in the cable net as well. Since the sag has to be rather large for acceptable tensions, the cable net assumes a flowing architectural form which may result in enormous headroom at the high points of the net. The heating of these spaces may pose special problems to the Architect.

The single cable had to be suitably anchored and imposed a large pull on the foundations. The cable net has to be upheld and supported by large columns and anchored at its ends. The cable net in this case operates on virtually the same principle as the circus tent. The load from the net enters the columns at points of support and is then transmitted to the foundations. Since the load from a very large surface area enters the column at a single point, the stress concentration at these points is very severe and a special reinforcing of the cable net has to be carried out to prevent the column from piercing the net. This reinforcing cable is shown in Fig. 189. The load on the columns is very large and this results in the column sections being massive as well.

13.2 Other tension structures

Tension structures need not necessarily be built only of cables or cable nets. They can also be built partially of solid, fabricated structural members which nevertheless still function as tension members. Examples of this are the two tension structures for the Minor Gymnasium and the Swimming Pool Facility for the Tokyo Olympic Games. The two structures are shown in Figs. 190 and 191. It is useful to verbalise the load propagation through these two beautiful tension structures.

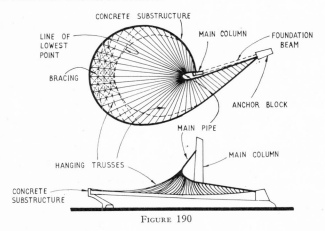

FIGURE 190

In the case of the roof over the Minor Gymnasium, and shown in Fig. 190, the roof tension members are hanging fabricated trusses about 24 in. deep which are anchored into a concrete substructure at one end and load onto the main tension pipe at the other. The tension pipe, which is about 16 in. in diameter, itself functions as a tension member. It loads onto the main central column at one end and is anchored at the other end in a massive anchor block. The pull of the main tension pipe on the main concrete column causes a tremendous overturning moment. In order to balance this, the weight of the anchor block is used as a counterweight, by connecting it to the main column through a foundation beam. The beam is shown dotted in Fig. 190. Finally in order to prevent flutter, the main tension pipe is braced against the main column and secondary bracing members are used to brace the hanging trusses. The whole structure is then roofed over with steel roof sheets about ⅛ in. thick which rest on the hanging trusses and the purlins and are spot welded to them.

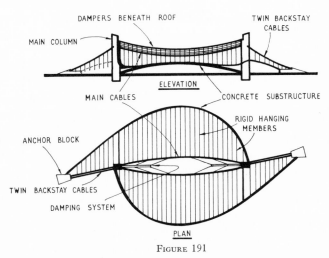

FIGURE 191

In the case of the suspension roof over the Swimming Pool facility, and shown in Fig. 191, the roof tension members are rigid, hanging I-section steel members, between 20 in. to 40 in. deep and spaced about 14 ft 9 in. on centers. They are anchored into a concrete substructure at one end and load onto two main central cables at the other. The main cables, which are each 13 in. in external diameter, are composed of 37 smaller cables and span 413 ft between the main concrete columns. They are splayed outwards and a damping system utilised between them to prevent flutter. The concrete columns are stabilised against the tremendous tensile pull of the main cables by twin backstay cables as shown in Fig. 191. These twin backstay cables span 144 ft and are anchored into massive anchor blocks. The entire structure is then roofed over with $\frac{3}{16}$ in. thick steel plates which are bolted to light gage steel rafters. The rafters then load the hanging girders at an interval of about 5 ft on centers. For clarity the rafters have not been shown in Fig. 191.

13.3 Pneumatic structures

Pneumatic structures, as their name implies, depend for their stability on air pressure. They are also sometimes termed as **inflatables**. This is also a structural form in which the membrane carries all its loads in pure tension in much the same way as a soap bubble or a child's balloon. These structures are becoming increasingly popular for the roofing of very large areas such as athletic facilities, green houses, etc. They also have special application for temporary structures such as exhibitions, since they can be deflated and re-used elsewhere again.

Pneumatic or inflatable structures are basically of two types.

1. Air supported structures.
2. Air inflated structures.

Air supported structures use internal air pressure to support the roof covering membrane as shown in Fig. 192. The air pressure differential between the inside and the outside of the structure is only of the order of $\frac{1}{500}$ atmospheric pressure. It is hence not noticeable to the occupants of the building but is sufficient to hold up the covering membrane. An air lock has to be provided to contain the air pressure and continuously operating fans or blowers are necessary to maintain it. Doors and windows need to be air sealed, but because the air pressure differential is very small, the actual loss of air through openings is small and can be easily handled by the fans. Snow loads, wind loads and incidental live loads can all be easily taken by slight increases in air pressure. The greatest danger lies in vandalism and rupture of the membrane. For this reason, the membrane used is a tough light plastics cloth membrane that can be wire reinforced for additional strength and durability.

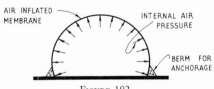

FIGURE 192

Air inflated structures work on the principle of the bicycle tube. When deflated the tube has no structural strength. When inflated under high pressure however, the tube springs into shape and has considerable strength. Air inflated structures consist of sealed tubes under high pressure which under inflation erect themselves into place. Such a structure is shown in Fig. 193. The air pressure is about 100 psi. Since the tubes are sealed, the membrane itself is not under air pressure and merely forms the roof covering. Air inflated structures therefore do not need air locks or continuous blower operation.

A third type of pneumatic structure called the **hybrid** air structure has

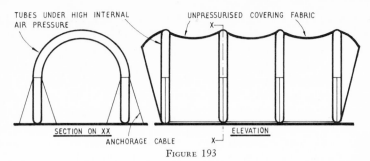

FIGURE 193

been defined in the literature. It is merely a combination of an inflated roof together with conventional wall or supporting framework.

In all types of pneumatic structures, anchorage is of some importance. The air pressure in an air supported structure causes an uplift that has to be adequately resisted by the foundations. The structure has to be weighted or tied down to ensure safety. This can be carried out by earth or water berms as shown in Fig. 192. The air inflated structure can be anchored by cables as shown in Fig. 193.

13.4 Air inflated nets

It has been seen in 13.3 and shown in Fig. 192 that under air pressure, the inflatable assumes a balloon shape with a very large rise. This increases tremendously the headroom at the center—often much more than required or desired by the Architect. This also increases considerably the volume under the inflatable all of which may have to be heated. This also increases the maintenance costs of the structure.

In order to overcome this disadvantage of the pure inflatable, it is possible to use an air inflated net which is a combination of an inflatable with

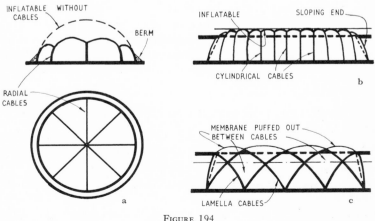

FIGURE 194

a tension net. The tension net determines the shape that the Architect wishes to have when the structure is finally inflated, as shown in Fig. 194. The membrane is inflated as before, lifting the cable net with it. When the final shape, depending on the lengths of the cables, is reached, the air pressure forces the cables into tension, thereby holding the inflatable down. The inflatable membrane is puffed out between the cables. The headroom and the internal volume can be suitably controlled. Fig. 194a shows the use of radial cables with a structure that is circular in plan. The air inflated net, shown in Fig. 194b, can be used for rectangular areas. Cylindrical cables are used to keep down the headroom. For more architectural appeal, lamella cables can also be used as shown in Fig. 194c. In all of the above cases, the cables serve to partially anchor the structure as well.

In all air supported structures, there arises a problem associated with the failure of the air compressor or a power failure. This would cause the structure to deflate. The problem is not really as serious as it seems, since the structure being under such a small differential air pressure, does not deflate instantly, giving sufficient warning for the building to be evacuated. In very important structures, safety precautions can be taken. Consider the hybrid air supported inflatable structure shown in Fig. 195. The structure is so

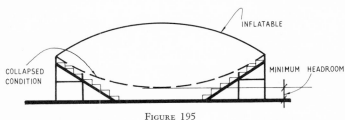

FIGURE 195

designed that even with a fully deflated membrane, a certain minimum headroom can still be maintained. The collapsed condition of the membrane is shown dotted in Fig. 195. If the inflatable is to be set at ground level, the arena could of course be set in a pit for the same effect. Finally it is always possible to provide in any of these structures, a secondary independent light structural system to hold up the sagging membrane if accidentally deflated, thereby ensuring a minimum headroom in the enclosure.

13.5 The integration of the structure into the architectural design

The integration of any structure into the architectural design is always desirable. For very large tension structures, or space structures of the type considered in Chapter 12, this may not always be easy. In the author's opinion, the integration is best done by designing the architecture around the structure itself. The structure by virtue of its size and shape may be visually the most important feature of the architectural design. The structure cannot be hidden. It dominates the architectural piece. This domination can be subdued or emphasized. For instance, by the use of translucent sheets as the roof covering, the cable lines can be made prominent. This applies particularly when the roof covering runs along the cable lines. In the case of double layered space structures, the roof covering can be placed on the top chord or below the bottom chord. In special cases, the roof covering can even be placed along the diagonals between top and bottom chords. The visual effect is different in each case. If desired, a flat double layered space deck can be hidden, but it requires the use of a false ceiling and deep fascia panels. This can be expensive. Associated with the problem of structure integration is also the problem of side enclosure. The cable net, like the hypar, does present problems of side enclosure where as the inflatable does not.

In all such cases of large space or tension structures, the domination of the visual architectural expression by the structure is almost total and complete. Whether Architecture then loses or gains by the domination of the structure is a matter that the individual Architect, motivated by his own personal philosophy of design, must decide for himself.